POC

R/T Communications Manual

Helena Hughes

Nothing in this manual supersedes any legislation, rules, regulations or procedures contained in any operational document issued by Her Majesty's Stationery Office, the Civil Aviation Authority, the Joint Aviation Authorities, ICAO, the manufacturers of aircraft, engines and systems, or by the operators of aircraft throughout the world.

R/T Communications Manual - Helena Hughes

Pooley Aviation Ltd
Mill Road
Cranfield
Bedfordshire
MK43 0JG
England

Tel: 01234 750677
Fax: 01234 750706
sales@pooleys.com
www.pooleys.com

Acknowledgments

This publication could not have been made possible without the valuable contribution of many friends and colleagues. Particularly, we would like to thank Nicolas Chan, David Duckworth, Peter Godwin and Robert Spencer. Many others have offered their thoughts and advice, too many to mention, but we must also thank the CAA who offered their support throughout.

Preface

This manual is aimed primarily at those wishing to undertake the radiotelephony written and practical examinations. At the time of going to press the most recent version of all phraseologies has been included, however as phraseology and procedures are often revised or amended, the current edition of CAP413 and JAR FCL-1 should be referenced.

It should be noted by students for the private pilots licence that although some of the material may seem to be outside the scope of your syllabus, the radio licence is the same whether you are a private pilot flying a two-seater trainer or an airline pilot flying an Airbus.

Editorial Team

AUTHOR
Helena Hughes BA(Hons)
Helena Hughes was born into an aviation household, having her first informal "flying lesson" at the age of four. Her late father David was a flying instructor and also flew corporate jets. On leaving University in 1989 Helena went to America to obtain a PPL, converting to a UK licence on return. Shortly afterwards she started work in Air Traffic Control at London Luton Airport earning her Controllers licence in 1990. During her time at Luton she was involved in controller training as both an Instructor and Assessor. Helena continues to be an operational Air Traffic Control Officer and is currently posted to Heathrow working "Thames Radar" and "Heathrow Special". She holds a CPL/IR and has been a flying instructor for the past 5 years teaching PPL and associated ratings. She is also a Ground and Radio Telephony Examiner.

EDITORS
Dorothy Pooley LLB(Hons) FRAeS
The author of Volume 1, Flying Training, Dorothy holds an ATPL and is an instructor and examiner, running flying instructor courses at Shoreham. She is a CAA Flight Instructor Examiner. Additionally she is an aviation solicitor acting as a consultant to ASB Law.

Daljeet Gill BA(Hons)
Daljeet is Head of Design & Development for Pooleys Flight Equipment. Editor of the Pooleys Private Pilots Guides by David Cockburn, Pre-flight Briefing (Aeroplanes), R/T Communications, Pooleys JAR Manuals plus many others. Daljeet has been involved with editing, typesetting and design for these publications. Graduated in 1999 with a BA (hons) in Graphic Design, she deals with marketing, advertising & design of our new products. She maintains our website and produces our Pooleys Catalogue annually.

Nicholas Chan
Nick obtained his PPL in 1998. He was then successful in winning the highly sought-after Somers Award, a scholarship administered by the Guild of Air Pilots and Air Navigators. This enabled Nick to study for and gain his Airline Transport Pilot's Licence, which he completed in March 2001. Whilst waiting for an airline job Nick studied for his flying instructor rating with Dorothy Pooley, where he displayed his talent for illustration and design, assisting Dorothy to improve the presentation of her Pre-flight briefings. Nick is now flying as a First Officer with British Airways.

Contents

Chapter 3 101

Chapter 4 141

Chapter 5 165

Chapter 6 181

Chapter 1

General Operating Procedures

Used correctly radio communications assist in the safe and efficient operation of aircraft. Employing a good technique and standard phraseology are the basis for reliable and unambiguous communications between air and ground stations regardless of the native tongue of their users. Poor communication procedures have been a contributory factor to both incidents and accidents over the years. Although the jargon and procedures may seem daunting at first the more you practise the easier it becomes!

Radio Installation

Your flying instructor will explain thoroughly how the radio installation in your aircraft works. The following is a very brief guide to some of the more common features.

On/Off - either a separate switch or may be combined with the volume control.
Freq Selection - rotating switching, two concentric knobs.
The outer selects MHz and the inner the decimals or KHz.

Outer Dial
123. 129. 132.

Inner Dial
.15 .07 .55

Digital Presentation

Frequency
Select to
Adjust
Standby

Pull for 25KHz

Transfer active to
Standby & Vice Versa

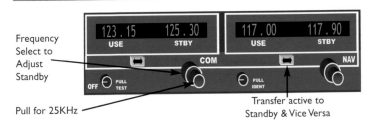

Selection Box

When an aircraft is fitted with more than one radio, each radio has a selector switch, to determine which is used.

The 'Auto' switch will select automatically the receiver belonging to the chosen transmitter in the illustration above COM 1 or 'Box 1'

a. Before Transmitting:

    i.   **Think** about what you are going to say!

    ii.   Check that the receiver volume is satisfactory.

    iii. **Listen out** on the frequency to be used, to ensure that you will not transmit over another station.

b. Maintain the microphone at a constant distance from your mouth. If using a hand held microphone also avoid turning your head whilst speaking. In either case allowing the microphone to touch your lips can seriously distort transmitted speech.

c. Speak in a normal conversational tone of voice – shouting also distorts the transmitted signal.

d. Speak at an even rate, around 100 words per minute at a maximum. The recipient may have to write down your details, if you know this is the case speak more slowly.

e. Maintain a constant volume.

f. Avoid using hesitation sounds such as "er" and "um".

g. On commencement, ensure that the transmit switch is fully depressed and ensure that you do not release it until you have finished speaking, this will ensure that your message is not "clipped".

h. Enunciate each word clearly and distinctly; remember that the first language of the recipient may not be the same as yours.

Finally, always ensure that you have released the transmit button after your message. This will avoid blocking a frequency, not only a great annoyance and potential danger, but possibly a great embarrassment, you may inadvertently broadcast something you do not want the rest of the world to hear!

Transmission of Letters

The phonetic alphabet is used when individual letters are to be transmitted. Phonetic spelling is sometimes used where there is a chance of ambiguity. The syllables to be emphasised are underlined.

Letter	Word	Pronunciation
A	ALPHA	AL FAH
B	BRAVO	BRAH VOH
C	CHARLIE	CHAR LEE or SHAR LEE
D	DELTA	DELL TAH
E	ECHO	ECK OH
F	FOXTROT	FOKS TROT
G	GOLF	GOLF
H	HOTEL	HOH TELL
I	INDIA	IN DEE AH
J	JULIET	JEW LEE ETT
K	KILO	KEY LOH
L	LIMA	LEE MAH
M	MIKE	MIKE
N	NOVEMBER	NO VEM BER
O	OSCAR	OSS CAH
P	PAPA	PAH PAH
Q	QUEBEC	KEH BECK
R	ROMEO	ROW ME OH
S	SIERRA	SEE AIR RAH
T	TANGO	TANG GO
U	UNIFORM	YOU NEE FORM
V	VICTOR	VIK TAH
W	WHISKY	WISS KEY
X	X-RAY	ECKS RAY
Y	YANKEE	YANG KEE
Z	ZULU	ZOO LOO

The syllables to be emphasised are underlined.

Numeral or Numeral Element	Pronunciation
0	ZERO
1	WUN
2	TOO
3	TREE
4	FOW ER
5	FIFE
6	SIX
7	SEV EN
8	AIT
9	NIN ER
Decimal	DAYSEEMAL
Hundred	HUNDRED
Thousand	TOUSAND

With some exceptions all numbers are transmitted by pronouncing each digit separately. The table below illustrates how numbers are transmitted for callsigns, flight levels, headings, wind velocity, transponder codes, runways and altimeter settings.

Number	Transmitted as
Aircraft Callsign BAL 455 EZY 203	Britannia four five five Easy two zero three
Flight Levels FL 180 FL 210	Flight level one eight zero Flight level two one zero
Note: The exceptions are flight levels involving whole hundreds e.g. FL100 "Flight level one hundred" FL200 "Flight level two hundred" etc.	
Headings 100° 280°	Heading one zero zero Heading two eight zero
Wind direction & Speed 340/12KT 090/15G32KT	Wind three four zero, one two knots Wind zero niner zero degrees, one five gusting three two knots
Transponder Codes 4662 7013	Squawk four six six two Squawk seven zero one three
Runway 26 07	Runway two six Runway zero seven
Altimeter Setting QNH 1010 QFE 995 mb	QNH one zero one zero QFE niner niner fife millibars
Note: 1) In the UK pressure setting 1000mb maybe transmitted as "**wun tou sand**" 2) Whenever a pressure setting below 1000 mb is broadcast the word "**millibar**" must be used following the digits.	

The exceptions to the above relate to the transmission of altitude, height, cloud height, visibility and runway visual range *(basically anything measured in feet or metres!).* In these cases whole hundreds and thousands are transmitted by stating the number of hundreds and thousands followed by the word **"HUN-dred"** or **"TOU-SAND"** as applicable. Combinations follow the same rule.

Number	Transmitted as
Altitude 900ft 2400ft 14,000ft	 Altitude niner hundred feet Altitude two thousand four hundred feet Altitude one four thousand feet
Cloud height 3200ft 5500ft	 Three thousand two hundred feet Five thousand five hundred feet
Visibility 1000m 700m	 Visibility one thousand metres Visibility seven hundred metres
RVR 400m 900m	 RVR four hundred metres RVR niner hundred metres

If a number contains a decimal point, as frequencies always do, the RTF word DAY-SEE-MAL is inserted at the appropriate point:

Number	Transmitted as	Pronounced as
121.1	One two one decimal one	Wun too wun dayseemal wun
120.925	One two zero decimal nine two	Wun too zero dayseemal niner too

Note: Only the first five digits are transmitted when identifying VHF frequencies.

Transmission of Time

Co-ordinated Universal Time (UTC) is to be used at all times, UTC is also known as Zulu and is the same as GMT. Normally when transmitting time only the minutes of the hour are required. If there is a possibility of confusion the hour should be included as well. Time checks will be given to the nearest minute.

Time	Transmitted as	Pronounced as:
0905	ZERO FIVE (or zero nine zero five)	ZERO FIFE
1400	ONE FOUR ZERO ZERO	WUN FOW-ER ZERO ZERO
2148	FOUR EIGHT (or two one four eight)	FOW-ER AIT

Standard Words and Phrases

The following words and phrases are used in radiotelephony communications and have the specific meanings listed below:

Word/Phrase	Meaning
ACKNOWLEDGE	Let me know that you have received and understood this message
AFFIRM	Yes
APPROVED	Permission for proposed action granted
BREAK	Indicates the separation between messages
BREAK BREAK	Indicates the separation between messages in a busy environment
CANCEL	Annul the previously transmitted clearance

CHANGING TO	I intend to call (unit) on (frequency)
CHECK	Examine a system or procedure
CLEARED	Authorised to proceed under the conditions specified
CLIMB	Climb and maintain
CONFIRM	Have I correctly received the following..? Did you correctly receive the following..?
CONTACT	Establish radio contact with
CORRECT	That is correct
CORRECTION	An error has been made in this transmission (or message indicated). The correct version is..
DESCEND	Descend and maintain
DISREGARD	Consider that message as not sent
GO AHEAD	Proceed with your message *This phrase is not normally used in surface movement communications. In the UK the phrase "Pass your message" is used instead.*
HOW DO YOU READ	What is the readability of my transmission?
I SAY AGAIN	I repeat for clarity or emphasis
MONITOR	Listen out on (frequency)
NEGATIVE	No; or permission not granted; or that is not correct
OUT	My transmission is ended and no response is expected. *This word is not normally used in U/VHF communications.*
OVER	My transmission is ended and I expect a response from you. *This word is not normally used in U/VHF communications.*

READBACK	Repeat all, or the specified part, of this message back to me exactly as received
REPORT	Pass me the following information
REQUEST	I should like to know.., or I wish to obtain
ROGER	I have received all of your last transmission **Note:** Under no circumstances should this word be used in reply to a question requiring a direct answer in the affirmative (AFFIRM) or negative (NEGATIVE), or to acknowledge any item requiring a readback.
SAY AGAIN	Repeat all, or the following part of your last transmission
SPEAK SLOWER	Reduce your rate of speech
STANDBY	Wait and I will call you **Note:** No onward clearance is to be assumed and **no response is expected**
VERIFY	Check and confirm
WILCO	I understand your message and will comply with it (an abbreviation of "will comply")
WORDS TWICE	*As a request* – communication is difficult. Please send every word twice. *As Information* – Since communication is difficult, every word of this message will be sent twice

Establishment and Continuation of Communication

When establishing communication the **full callsigns** of both the aircraft and the aeronautical station must be used.

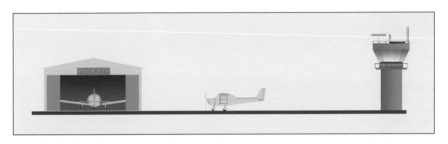

Luton Ground
Golf-Charlie Juliet Juliet Sierra

Golf-Charlie Juliet Juliet Sierra **Luton Ground** go ahead

Note: In the UK **"pass your message"** is used and has the same meaning as the ICAO phrase "**go ahead**"

Provided that no ambiguity or confusion will result, once contact has been established continuous communication may be carried out without further identification.

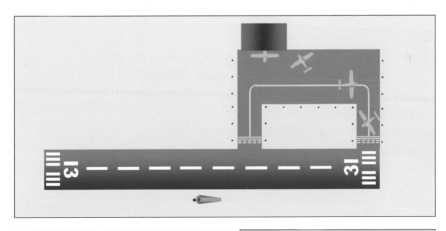

Golf-Charlie Juliet juliet Sierra request taxi

Golf-Juliet Sierra taxi Bravo one runway three one

Once the ground station has abbreviated your callsign you are at liberty to do likewise.

Golf-Juliet Sierra
taxi Bravo one runway three one

Placement of Callsigns

Ground to Air:
Aircraft callsign followed by message or reply

Air to Ground:

Initiation of new information/request – aircraft callsign then message

Example

Golf-Juliet Sierra
request descent

Reply:
Repeat Information / Readback / Acknowledgement then Aircraft Callsign

Example

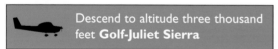

Descend to altitude three thousand feet **Golf-Juliet Sierra**

Aircraft will normally be advised by the appropriate ATCU to change from one radio frequency to another.

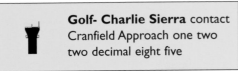

Golf- Charlie Sierra contact Cranfield Approach one two two decimal eight five

Cranfield Approach one two two decimal eight five **Golf- Charlie Sierra**

In the absence of such advice the aircraft should notify the ATCU before changing frequency, and if flying within **controlled airspace** must obtain **permission** before leaving a frequency.

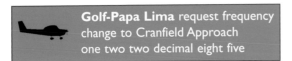

Golf-Papa Lima request frequency change to Cranfield Approach one two two decimal eight five

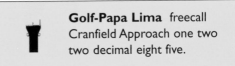

Golf-Papa Lima freecall Cranfield Approach one two two decimal eight five.

"Contact" means that your flight details have been passed to the next controlling authority and they expect your call. **"Freecall"** means that no flight details have been passed ahead and it is up to you to pass them once communication has been established.

An aircraft may be instructed to "**standby**" on a frequency, the intention here is that the ATSU in question will initiate further contact.

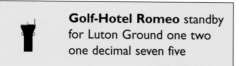

Golf-Hotel Romeo standby
for Luton Ground one two
one decimal seven five

Standby Luton Ground one
two one decimal seven five
Golf-Hotel Romeo

An aircraft may also be instructed to "**monitor**" a frequency on which information is being broadcast.

Even if the category of airspace does not dictate that an aircraft must remain in contact with a specific ATSU, if the pilot wishes to call another station s/he should request or notify such an intention. Not only is this polite, but also once two way communication has been established with an ATSU a flight is automatically in receipt of an alerting service *(see page 104)*. One of the "alert" items is "radio contact lost", therefore should you "disappear" from their frequency without notice, the ATSU would then be duty bound to inform the appropriate agencies and try to ascertain your whereabouts.

Issuance of Clearance & Readback Requirements

Relevant Definitions:

Air Traffic Control Clearance

Authorisation for an aircraft to proceed under conditions specified by an air traffic control unit.

Clearance Limit

The point to which an aircraft is granted an air traffic control clearance

A clearance may vary in complexity from a detailed description of the route and levels to be flown (at busier airports condensed to standard instrument departures) to a brief landing clearance. Clearances are required for any flight, or portion of flight for which an air traffic control or an air traffic advisory service is provided.

Controllers will endeavour to pass the clearance slowly and clearly since the pilot needs to write it down, hopefully avoiding the need for wasteful repetition. For preference route clearances will be given before engine start when the crew workload is lower. Controllers will avoid passing clearances when aircraft are involved in complicated taxi manoeuvres and particularly during line-up or take off. The aircraft's **full callsign** should be used by both ATC and the pilot.

> Note: An ATC route clearance **is not** authorisation to enter or take off on an active runway. The words "take-off" are only used when an aircraft is actually cleared for take off or when take-off clearance is cancelled. Careful phraseology has been developed to avoid any ambiguity and controllers will use the words   **"DEPARTURE"** and **"AIRBORNE"** at all other times.

Contents of a Clearance

- Aircraft identification
- Clearance limit
- Route
- Level of flight and changes of level*

The following may be included:

- ATFM slot
- Time restrictions
- Communication instructions
- Any special instructions e.g. approach or departure manoeuvres

* *Changes of level may be passed as either:*

a.	**Request level change en-route**
b.	**Climb when instructed by radar**
c.	**Temporary climb restriction**

The only significance of the above is that the procedures followed by IFR Flights in the event of a Radio Communications failure will differ depending on which level change restriction they were issued.

An aircraft may be cleared for its entire route to the first aerodrome of intended landing if it is to remain within controlled airspace for the entire flight and reasonable assurance exists that prior co-ordination can take place between ATCUs ahead of the aircraft's passage.

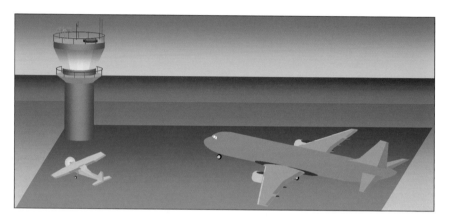

Example 1 **IFR Clearance**

Modernair three two one bravo cleared to destination Bournemouth, standard departure route Papa, climb to altitude four thousand feet, squawk five four three six, frequency Luton Radar one two niner decimal five five.

Cleared to Bournemouth standard departure route Papa, climb to altitude four thousand feet, squawk five four three six frequency Luton Radar one two niner decimal five five **Modernair three two one bravo**

Modernair 321B readback correct

Example 2 **VFR Clearance**

> Golf-Charlie Juliet Juliet Sierra
> cleared to the northern zone
> boundary, VFR, left turn after
> departure route northern lane not
> above altitude one thousand five
> hundred feet QNH one zero
> zero two.

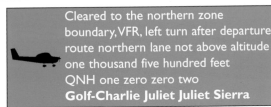

> Cleared to the northern zone
> boundary, VFR, left turn after departure
> route northern lane not above altitude
> one thousand five hundred feet
> QNH one zero zero two
> **Golf-Charlie Juliet Juliet Sierra**

> Golf-Juliet Sierra readback correct

Readback Requirements

Readback requirements were introduced in the interests of flight safety to ensure that the message has been received correctly as intended. The stringency of the requirement is directly related to the possible seriousness of a misunderstanding. Reading back also ensures that the correct aircraft and that aircraft alone will act upon the instruction given.

The ATC messages listed below **must be read back in full.** If a pilot fails to readback any of these items the controller will ask him/her to do so. Likewise, the pilot should request that any instructions that have not been fully understood be repeated or clarified.

a. **Level instructions**
b. **Heading instructions**
c. **Speed instructions**
d. **Airways or route clearances**
e. **Approach clearances**
f. **Runway in use**

g.   **Clearances to enter, land on, take off from, backtrack, cross or hold short of an active runway**
h.   **SSR operating instructions**
i.   **Altimeter settings**
j.   **VDF information**
k.   **Frequency changes**
l.   **Type of radar service**

The pilot should terminate the readback with the aircraft callsign. Items not in the above list may be acknowledged with an abbreviated readback.

If the readback is incorrect the controller will transmit the word **"NEGATIVE"** followed by the correct version.

Golf-Delta Charlie
QNH one zero zero two

QNH one zero one two
Golf-Delta Charlie

Golf-Delta Charlie
negative QNH one zero zero two

QNH one zero zero two
Golf-Delta Charlie

If at any time a pilot receives an instruction or clearance with which he cannot comply, the controller should be advised using the phrase **"UNABLE TO COMPLY"** or simply the word **"UNABLE"** together with the reason. Where doubt exists as to whether an instruction or clearance is possible the controller may end the message with **"IF NOT POSSIBLE ADVISE"**

Britannia seven one two climb flight level three four zero

Britannia seven one two unable climb flight level three four zero due weight

Or

Golf November Tango squawk four six six seven

Unable to comply negative transponder **Golf November Tango**

Level Instructions

The phraseology used when referring to vertical position differs depending on the pressure setting in use:

If QFE is set: "Height ..... ft"
If QNH is set: "Altitude ..... ft"
If standard 1013mb is set: "Flight Level ....."

Additionally, if instructed or requesting climb or descent to a Flight Level the word **"TO"** is omitted.

Golf-Juliet Sierra request climb flight level three five

As opposed to:

Golf-Juliet Sierra request climb **TO** altitude three thousand five hundred feet

Regional Pressure Settings will be passed in the following format: Region Name (pressure) e.g.

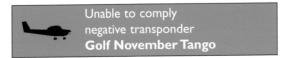
Golf-Hotel Hotel Cotswold 1002

The word 'millibar' **must** be used when transmitting all pressure settings below 1000mb e.g. QNH 994 millibars - this is to avoid any confusion with inches of mercury, the datum used in the United States.

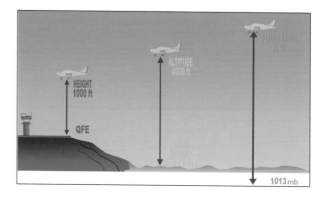

Lastly, one other type of clearance that must be read back is a **Conditional Clearance.** Conditional clearances will not be used for movements affecting the active runway(s) except when the aircraft or vehicles concerned are visible to both the controller and the pilot/driver concerned. Conditional clearances relate to one movement only and if it relates to a landing aircraft this will be the first on the approach and next to land.

Conditional clearances are given in the following order:

- **Callsign**
- **The Condition**
- **The Clearance**

Example 1

> **Golf-Juliet Sierra**
> after the landing Boeing seven three
> seven on 3 mile final backtrack,
> line up runway two five

Example 2

> After the landing Boeing seven
> three seven backtrack and line up
> runway two five **Golf-Juliet Sierra**

> **Golf-Juliet Sierra** after an
> outbound Cessna one seven two taxiing
> left to right, taxi to stand three four.

> After the Cessna one seven
> two taxi stand three four
> **Golf-Juliet Sierra**

Radiotelephony Callsigns for Aircraft

An aircraft callsign must follow one of the following styles. **Full Callsigns** must be used when:

a. **Establishing Communication**
b. **Reading back an ATC Route Clearance**
c. **Requested by ATC**

Full Callsigns

Type	Example
1. The characters corresponding to the registration marking of the aircraft.	G-CJJS or N111VP Piper G-CJJS* Citation G-HBAH*
2. The telephony designator of the aircraft operating agency, followed by the last four characters of the registration marking of the aircraft.	Modernair GBNPL Britannia GBYAE
3. The telephony designator of the aircraft operating agency, followed by the flight identification.	Modernair 012 Monarch 416

* Either the manufacturer's name or the name of aircraft model may be used to prefix the callsign.

Once satisfactory communication is established, and provided that no confusion is likely, the callsign may be abbreviated. The pilot of an aircraft may **only** abbreviate the callsign if the relevant aeronautical ground station has abbreviated it first.

Abbreviated Callsigns

Type		Example
1.	The first and at least the last two characters of the aircraft registration.	G-JS or N1VP Piper JS Citation AH
2.	The telephony designator of the aircraft operating agency, followed by at least the last two characters of the registration marking of the aircraft.	Modernair PL Britannia AE
3.	No abbreviation permitted.	Modernair 012 Monarch 416

An aircraft may not change its callsign type during flight. Where there is likelihood of confusion ATC may instruct an aircraft to change its callsign temporarily. When the possibility of confusion no longer exists the aircraft will be instructed to revert to the callsign specified in the original flight plan.

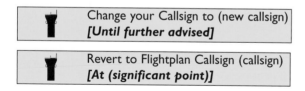

Change your Callsign to (new callsign)
[Until further advised]

Revert to Flightplan Callsign (callsign)
[At (significant point)]

Aircraft classified in the heavy wake turbulence category must include the word **"HEAVY"** immediately after the callsign in the initial call to each ATSU.

London Control
Britannia 767F Heavy

Aeronautical stations are identified by:

a.   **The name of the location, and**
b.   **A suffix denoting the type of unit or service available**

The name of the location or the unit/service may be omitted once satisfactory communication has been established and there is no likelihood of confusion.

Unit	Callsign Suffix	Service
Area control centre	CONTROL	ATC
Radar (general)	RADAR	ATC
Approach control	APPROACH	ATC
Approach control radar arrivals	ARRIVAL/DIRECTOR	ATC
Approach control radar departures	DEPARTURE	ATC
Aerodrome control	TOWER	ATC
Surface movement control	GROUND	ATC
Clearance delivery	DELIVERY	ATC
Precision approach radar	PRECISION/TALKDOWN	ATC
Direction finding station	HOMER	ATC
Flight information service	INFORMATION	FISO
Aeronautical station	RADIO	A/G

Additionally there are some frequencies used by aeronautical companies:

Apron control/management service	APRON	Operations
Company dispatch	DISPATCH	Operations

There are three main categories of aeronautical communications service:

a. Air Traffic Control (ATC)

Provided by licensed Air Traffic Control Officers (**ATCOs**) who undergo an extensive training programme and are closely regulated by the CAA in much the same way flight crew are. Their performance is regularly checked, they undergo continuation training and the actual hours they are allowed to work are strictly regulated. Only a controller is permitted to issue a **clearance**. Pilots must comply with instructions given by ATC - unless there is a really compelling reason not to!

b. Flight Information Service

At aerodromes, provided by licensed Flight Information Service Officers (**FISOs**) who have to take some less stringent examinations and are tested at less regular intervals than ATCOs.

The phraseology used by FISOs is different from that used by controllers. Flight Information Service (**FIS**) provided for the safe and efficient conduct of flights in the Aerodrome Traffic Zone. From this information pilots will be able to decide the appropriate course of action to be taken to ensure the safety of flight. ie. The onus is on you, the pilot, to decide.

The Flight Information Service Officer is not permitted to issue instructions to pilots of his own volition. However, FISOs provide positive control whilst aircraft are on the ground, in the air information only will be passed to assist pilots to operate safely and efficiently within the ATZ. FIS is available at aerodromes during the hours of operation indicated in the UK AIP. The service is easily identifiable by the callsign suffix **'information'**.

c. Air/ground Communications Service (A/G)

Provided by Radio Operators who are not licensed but hold a certificate of competency to operate radio equipment on aviation frequencies from the CAA. From an air/ground station only limited airfield information is available i.e. runway in use, surface wind, possibly pressure settings if suitable equipment is available. The callsign suffix **"Radio"** is used.

At aerodromes where a frequency has been allocated but no ground station is established, or the ground station is closed, calls should still be addressed to: **"(Location) Radio"**

Definition:
Air/Ground Communications Service (A/G)
A service that permits information to be passed from an aeronautical station to an aircraft on or in the vicinity of an aerodrome.

As the majority of this manual is concerned with ATC Communications, however, some extended examples of the phraseologies used by FISOs and AGCS operators are included at the end of the chapter concerning aerodrome operations, these may also be found in CAP 413.

Categories of Message

Relevant Definitions:
Aeronautical Mobile Service
A radio communication service between aircraft stations and aeronautical stations, or between aircraft stations. (CAP 413).

The Aeronautical Mobile Service handles messages in the following order of priority:

Message Category & Order of Priority	RT Signal
1. Distress Calls, Distress Messages and Distress Traffic.	MAYDAY
2. Urgency Messages, including messages preceded by the Medical Transports Signal.	PAN PAN PAN PAN MEDICAL
3. Communications relating to Direction Finding.	
4. Flight Safety Messages.	
5. Meteorological Messages.	
6. Flight regularity Messages.	

Distress Calls, Distress Messages and Distress Traffic

See Chapter 4

Urgency Messages

Including messages preceded by the medical transports signal - *See Chapter 4*

Communications relating to Direction Finding

Aircraft normally make the request for bearing, heading or position information from a ground station using the appropriate Q code.

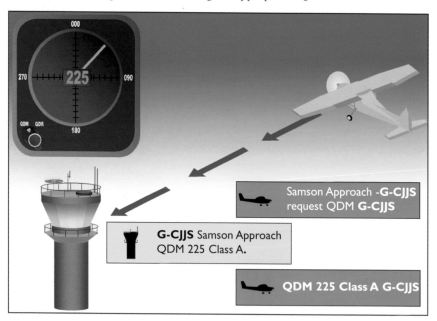

QDM	Aircraft's Magnetic Heading to steer to reach the Station.
	Note: No allowance is made for the wind vector.
QDR	Aircraft's Magnetic Bearing from the Station
QTE	Aircraft's True Bearing from the Station
QUJ	Aircraft's True Track to the Station

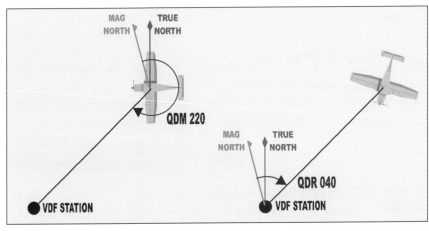

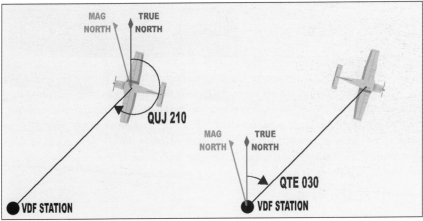

Accuracy of Bearings

Class A +/- 2 degrees
Class B +/- 5 degrees
Class C +/- 10 degrees
Class D accuracy less than class C

Phraseology

Aircraft requesting bearing information from a VDF station should use the following phraseology; repetition of the callsign ensures that the transmitted signal is of sufficient length for the ground equipment to establish a bearing. Since VDF information is an item that must be readback in full, a typical exchange would be:

Samson Approach -G-CJJS request QDM **G-CJJS**

G-CJJS Samson Approach QDM 225 Class A.

QDM 225 Class A G-CJJS

A direction finding station working alone will be able to give the preceding information i.e. bearing information relative to that particular station. They can, however, combine and work as a network to "**triangulate**" an aircraft's position. When performing this function, the controlling station receives the bearing information from each station at the same time enabling the aircraft's position to be determined. Additional broadcasts from the aircraft may be requested by the controlling station once the group of ground stations are ready.

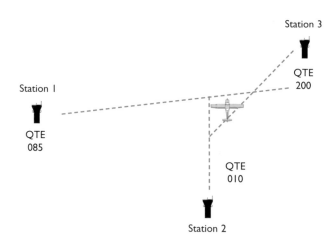

1.   What is the meaning of **"roger"** and **"wilco"**?

2.   State the correct abbreviation for the callsign:
     a.   MONARCH GMONY
     b.   GDIXY

3.   Define **"Aeronautical Station"**?

4.   How are:
     a.   Times 1355 and 1500
     b.   2400ft QNH
     c.   Frequency 126.725 transmitted?

5.   List the items that must be read back

6.   List the message priorities

7.   What are the main categories of aeronautical communications service?

8.   Duxford has an AFIS, what is their callsign?

9.   Bourn has an air/ground station, what is their callsign?

10.   When may you, as a pilot abbreviate the aircraft callsign?

11.   ATC asks if you are able to maintain FL50, what answers are possible?

12.   In messages relating to height or altitude the word "to" should be included where?

13.   List the items included in a conditional clearance?

14.   If given an instruction by ATC with which are not able to comply – your response should be what?

15.   State the different words used to differentiate between vertical position when using:
     i. QFE
     ii. QNH
     iii. 1013mb

16.   When must your aircraft's full callsign be used?

Left Intentionally Blank

Chapter 2

Aerodrome Procedures

Aerodromes Procedures

Clear and concise phraseology is vital to the safe and efficient operation of an aerodrome. Although precise procedures vary from place to place the following is an overview of general VFR aerodrome communications. Details of local requirements can be found in the UK Air Pilot, Pooleys Flight Guide or similar publication.

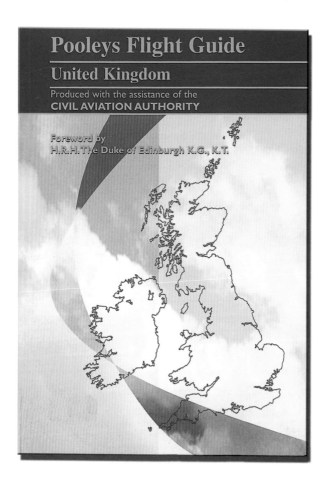

There are also slight differences in phraseology and procedure depending on the level of service provided at an aerodrome i.e. whether it is an ATC, FIS or simple air/ground station.

Chapter 2 - Part 1

Departure Information and Engine Start

ATIS

At busier airports an **Automatic Terminal Information Service** is broadcast to provide a range of data on a discreet frequency or selected VOR. This not only reduces frequency loading, but also enables the pilot to make an early decision about an approach or take off.

A solely **"Departure ATIS"** may be installed and is only to be used by aircraft on the ground as this frequency will have limited range protection. Controllers are required to obtain a readback of relevant pressure settings contained in the broadcast.

Each ATIS message is coded consecutively using the phonetic alphabet. A new message is generated at regular intervals *(usually half hourly at the time of the routine meteorological observations at minutes 20 and 50)* or whenever a significant change occurs.

Pilots of departing aircraft need only acknowledge receipt of an ATIS message when the broadcast includes a specific request to do so. Pilots of arriving aircraft are required to acknowledge receipt of the ATIS message on initial contact with approach control using the code letter specified in the ATIS broadcast. To avoid time-consuming repetition pilots should advise ATC that they have received the latest ATIS:

On Departure	–	before taxiing
On Arrival	–	on first contact with the ATSU.

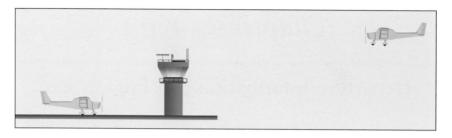

Departure

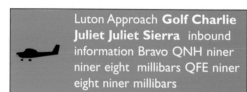

Luton Ground **Golf Charlie Juliet Juliet Sierra** request radio check one two one decimal seven five, information Bravo received QNH niner niner eight millibars

Golf Charlie Juliet Juliet Sierra **Luton Ground** readability five, Bravo current QNH correct.

Arrival

Luton Approach **Golf Charlie Juliet Juliet Sierra** inbound information Bravo QNH niner niner eight millibars QFE niner eight niner millibars

Golf Charlie Juliet Juliet Sierra **Luton Approach** bravo current, enter the control zone VFR not above altitude two thousand feet QNH niner niner eight millibars

Enter control zone VFR not above altitude two thousand feet QNH niner niner eight millibars **Golf Charlie Juliet Juliet Sierra**

An ATIS message should contain all or some of the following items of information in the order listed:

- **Name of the aerodrome**
- **Runway in use**
  (and after type of approach to be expected eg. ILS/SRA.)
- **Code letter**
- **Time of the weather observation**
- **Weather**
- **Cloud**
- **Temperature and dew point**
- **QNH**
- **QFE (threshold QFE if applicable)**
- **Essential aerodrome information**
- **A repeat of the identifying letter**

Note: Rapidly changing situations may not be included in the ATIS broadcast; these will be passed by the controller to ensure the most up to date information is available.

Sample ATIS Broadcast

**This is London Luton information Papa at time one three five zero
Expect an ILS approach to runway two six
Surface wind three zero zero degrees one five knots, visibility eight
  kilometres, slight rain, cloud broken at one thousand two hundred
  feet, temperature +one zero dew point +seven, QNH one zero
  one four millibars threshold QFE runway two six one zero zero
  six millibars.
Taxiway Bravo is unavailable.
Report information Papa received and aircraft type on initial
  contact with Luton.**

Where no ATIS is available pilots may request the current aerodrome information before asking for start up:

Coventry Ground **Golf- Charlie Juliet Juliet Sierra** request departure information

Golf- Charlie Juliet Juliet Sierra **Coventry Ground** departure runway two three, surface wind one niner zero, one zero knots, visibility greater than one zero kilometres, temperature plus two two dew point plus four, QNH one zero zero niner

Runway two three , QNH one zero zero niner . Request start-up **Golf- Charlie Juliet Juliet Sierra**

Golf-Juliet Sierra start approved.

Requests to start engines help ATC plan the departure sequence and additionally prevent unnecessary fuel wastage, absorbing any delay with engines shut down. Including the parking position of the aircraft can also aid ATC in identifying the most expeditious departure order.

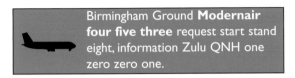

Birmingham Ground **Modernair four five three** request start stand eight, information Zulu QNH one zero zero one.

Modernair four five three **Birmingham Ground** start approved. Zulu current QNH correct.

Or

Modernair four five three **Birmingham Ground** expect start at time two seven. Zulu current QNH correct.

Or

Modernair four five three **Birmingham Ground** departure at time four six start approved when ready. Zulu current QNH correct.

Test Procedures and the Readability Scale

Test transmissions should take the following format:

- **The identification of the aeronautical station being called**
- **The aircraft callsign**
- **The words "radio check"**
- **The frequency being used**

Replies will be in the following form:

- **The identification of the station calling**
- **The identification of the station replying**
- **Information regarding the readability of the transmission**

The readability of the transmission is classified in accordance with the following scale, other information regarding the quality of the transmission that may be useful to the station requesting the test may also be added.

Readability Scale	Meaning
1	Unreadable
2	Readable now and then
3	Readable but with difficulty
4	Readable
5	Perfectly readable

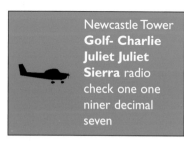

Newcastle Tower **Golf- Charlie Juliet Juliet Sierra** radio check one one niner decimal seven

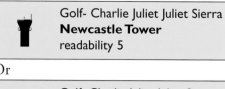

Golf- Charlie Juliet Juliet Sierra **Newcastle Tower** readability 5

Or

Golf- Charlie Juliet Juliet Sierra **Newcastle Tower** readability 3 with a loud background whistle

Or

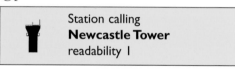

Station calling **Newcastle Tower** readability 1

Chapter 2 - Part 2

Taxi Instructions

Any taxi instructions issued by a controller will always include a clearance limit, this will be the point at which the aircraft **must** stop until further permission to proceed is given. Usually for a departing aircraft this will be the holding point for the runway in use.

At busier aerodromes there are often separate GROUND and TOWER frequencies. Unless contrary information is broadcast on the ATIS message, on departure initial contact should be made on the ground frequency. The ground controller is responsible for aircraft on the manoeuvring area up to the holding points to the runway in use. Outbound aircraft will be transferred to the TOWER as the aircraft is at or approaching the holding point.

So that no misunderstanding arises, unless an aircraft is actually being "Cleared for Take off" or that clearance is being cancelled, the word **"Departure"** will be used.

Example 1

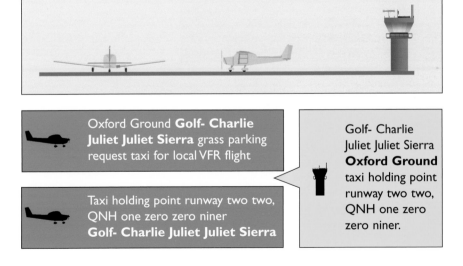

Oxford Ground **Golf- Charlie Juliet Juliet Sierra** grass parking request taxi for local VFR flight

Golf- Charlie Juliet Juliet Sierra **Oxford Ground** taxi holding point runway two two, QNH one zero zero niner.

Taxi holding point runway two two, QNH one zero zero niner **Golf- Charlie Juliet Juliet Sierra**

Example 2

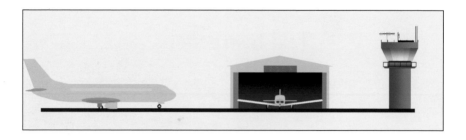

Luton Ground
Golf- Charlie Juliet Juliet Sierra
hangar 89 request taxi.

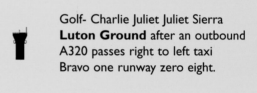

Golf- Charlie Juliet Juliet Sierra
Luton Ground after an outbound
A320 passes right to left taxi
Bravo one runway zero eight.

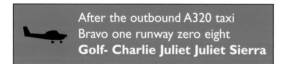

After the outbound A320 taxi
Bravo one runway zero eight
Golf- Charlie Juliet Juliet Sierra

Example 3

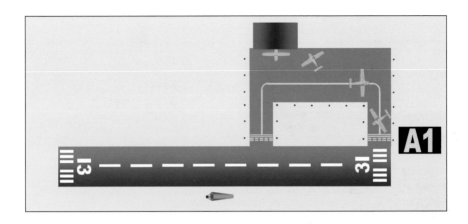

Golf- Juliet Sierra taxi holding point
Alpha one report ready for departure

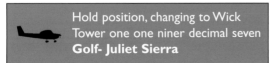
Taxi to Alpha one, wilco
Golf- Juliet Sierra

Golf- Juliet Sierra
ready for departure

Golf- Juliet Sierra hold position,
contact Wick Tower one one
niner decimal seven

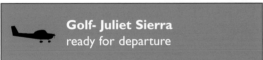
Hold position, changing to Wick
Tower one one niner decimal seven
Golf- Juliet Sierra

Left Intentionally Blank

Chapter 2 - Part 3

Take Off

Controllers will not transmit to an aircraft during the take off or initial climb out, unless it is absolutely essential. If more than one runway is in use, or the aircraft is not yet lined up the runway designator will be stated in the take off clearance.

 Golf- Juliet Sierra
ready for departure

 Golf- Juliet Sierra line up
and wait runway two seven

 Line up runway two seven
Golf- Juliet Sierra

 Golf- Juliet Sierra runway two
seven cleared for take off, left
turn out VFR, surface wind
three zero zero degrees
one four knots

 Cleared for take off runway
two seven, left turn out VFR
Golf- Juliet Sierra

If an expeditious departure is required the instruction **"Cleared immediate take off"** will be used. If the pilot accepts this clearance s/he should:

- If on the runway, begin the take off immediately
- If at the holding point, taxi onto the runway and take off without stopping

 Golf- Juliet Sierra are you ready for an immediate departure?

 Affirm **Golf- Juliet Sierra**

 Golf- Juliet Sierra runway two seven cleared immediate take off surface wind three zero zero degrees one four knots

 Cleared immediate take off **Golf- Juliet Sierra**

Or

 Golf- Juliet Sierra Boeing seven three seven 2 miles on final approach. Cleared immediate take off.

 Cleared immediate take off **Golf- Juliet Sierra**

In order to expedite traffic ATC are permitted to line up more than one aircraft on the same, or crossing runways, however there are certain conditions of which the controller must be satisfied:

- It must be daylight
- All the aircraft must be continuously visible to the controller
- All the aircraft must be on the same frequency
- The pilots are warned of their number in the departure sequence and the position/runway from which the traffic ahead will depart
- The physical characteristics of the runway do not render preceding aircraft invisible to those following

A **Conditional Clearance** may be issued to help the traffic flow. This will relate to one movement only, and if the subject aircraft is landing it must be the first on the approach. It is vital that the pilot has identified the subject aircraft correctly – if there is any doubt ask! The format will be:

- Callsign
- The condition
- Identification of the subject of the condition
- The instruction

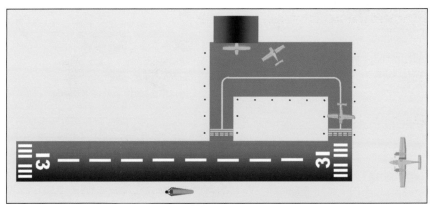

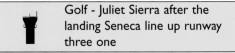
Golf - Juliet Sierra after the landing Seneca line up runway three one

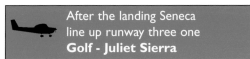
After the landing Seneca line up runway three one
Golf - Juliet Sierra

A conditional clearance **must** be readback.

If it is necessary to cancel a take off clearance the following phraseology used will be:

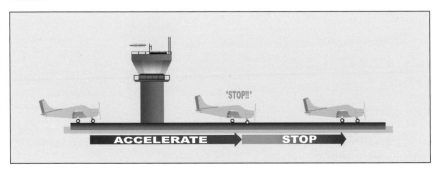

Aircraft Stationary:

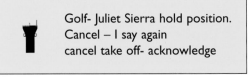

Golf- Juliet Sierra hold position.
Cancel – I say again
cancel take off- acknowledge

Aircraft Commenced
Take off:

Golf- Juliet Sierra stop
immediately – I say again
Golf- Juliet Sierra stop
immediately - acknowledge

As you can see this instruction must also be readback. The response **"stopping"** is all that is required, as depending on the circumstances the controller's workload may be quite high.

If the pilot abandons the take off, the tower should be advised as soon as it is safe to do so. Assistance or taxi instructions should be requested as required.

Pilot Abandons Take-off:

Golf- Juliet Sierra stopping

Golf- Juliet Sierra roger

Golf- Juliet Sierra request
return to apron

Golf- Juliet Sierra vacate next
right hold Hotel four.

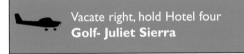

Vacate right, hold Hotel four
Golf- Juliet Sierra

Golf- Juliet Sierra contact
Samson Ground one one niner
decimal niner.

Samson Ground one one niner
decimal niner **Golf- Juliet Sierra**

If the visibility is poor the pilot may be asked to report airborne:

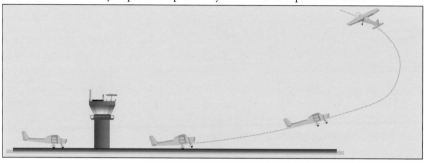

 Golf- Juliet Sierra cleared for take off report airborne

 Cleared for take off, Wilco
Golf- Juliet Sierra

Golf- Juliet Sierra airborne.

Golf- Juliet Sierra
contact Luton Radar 129.55

Different phraseology will be used at an aerodrome with an AFIS unit:

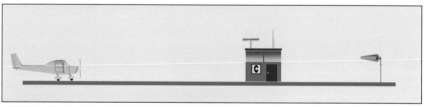

 **Golf- Juliet Sierra**
ready for departure

 Golf- Juliet Sierra **take off your discretion,**
surface wind zero niner zero, one four.

 Taking off **Golf- Juliet Sierra**

Or simply

Golf- Juliet Sierra

Notwithstanding the level of service provided, the ultimate decision as to whether it is safe to enter an active runway remains the pilot's responsibility. Even if given a clearance by ATC to enter the runway the pilot should always **CHECK** visually before doing so.

The vast majority of phraseology is the same for both rotary and fixed wing aircraft. Slight differences may be experienced by helicopter pilots in relation to departure and arrival, by virtue of not always having to use a runway. FISOs at aerodromes follow slightly different rules for helicopters, in that instructions can be passed to helicopters during air taxi even though the aircraft is technically airborne and should therefore receive information only.

 Cardiff Tower **Golf-Hotel Echo Lima India** radio check one two five decimal zero

 Golf-Hotel Echo Lima India Cardiff Tower readability five. Pass your message.

 Golf-Hotel Echo Lima India Robinson R22 west parking area, request taxi to the training area

 Golf-Lima India hover taxi to hold Echo one, surface wind one two zero, five knots.

 Air taxi Echo one, **Golf-Lima India**

 Golf-Lima India after the departing Boeing 737, runway three zero, cross the runway north to south, taxi to the training area

 After the departing Boeing 737, cross and taxi to training area **Golf-Lima India**

 Golf-Lima India request depart to the south

 Golf-Lima India lift approved*, surface wind one three zero, seven knots.

 Lift approved **Golf-Lima India**

*As long as the Aerodrome Controller has your aircraft in sight they may use **"Cleared for take off"** as per fixed wing. Similarly **"alight"** may be used instead of **"land"**. You will no doubt encounter both versions!

Left Intentionally Blank

Chapter 2 - Part 4

VFR Departure Scenario One – Control Zone Departure

Frequencies: ATIS 120.77   GROUND 121.25   TOWER 130.85

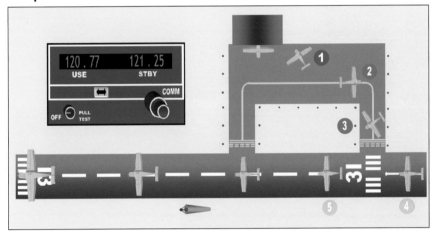

ATIS 120.77

This is Cranville information **X-ray** time one four two zero, expect an **ILS** approach to runway three one. Surface wind three six zero degrees one two knots, visibility eight thousand metres, cloud scattered two thousand five hundred feet, temperature plus one zero dew point plus four, **QNH** one zero zero two, **QFE** niner niner eight millibars. Report information **X-ray** received on first contact with Cranville **ATC**.

GROUND 121.25

Cranville Ground **Golf- Charlie Juliet Juliet Sierra**

Golf- Charlie Juliet Juliet Sierra **Cranville Ground**

Cranville Ground **Golf- Charlie Juliet Juliet Sierra** request radio check one two one decimal two five

Golf- Juliet Sierra readability five

Readability five also, information X-ray received QNH one zero zero two request taxi **Golf- Juliet Sierra**

Golf- Juliet Sierra taxi holding point runway three one.

Taxi holding point runway three one **Golf- Juliet Sierra**

Golf- Juliet Sierra zone departure clearance when ready

 Pass your message
Golf- Juliet Sierra

 Golf- Charlie Juliet Juliet Sierra after departure leave the control zone VFR own navigation climb not above altitude two thousand feet.

 After departure leave the control zone VFR own navigation climb not above altitude two thousand feet **Golf- Charlie Juliet Juliet Sierra.**

 Golf- Juliet Sierra readback correct, report ready for departure.

 Wilco **Golf- Juliet Sierra**

 Golf- Juliet Sierra ready for departure

3

 Golf- Juliet Sierra hold position contact Cranville Tower one three zero decimal eight five.

 Hold position contact Cranville Tower one three zero decimal eight five **Golf- Juliet Sierra**

TOWER 130.85

 Cranville Tower **Golf- Charlie Juliet Juliet Sierra**

 Golf- Charlie Juliet Juliet Sierra **Cranville Tower**, hold position. After the landing Airbus A320 two mile final backtrack, line up runway three one.

 4

 Holding position, after the landing A320 backtrack, line up runway three one **Golf- Charlie Juliet Juliet Sierra**

 Golf- Juliet Sierra cleared for take off, surface wind three five zero degrees one one knots.

 5

 Cleared for take off **Golf- Juliet Sierra**

 Golf- Juliet Sierra contact Cranville Radar One two four decimal zero seven

 Contact Cranville Radar One two four decimal zero seven **Golf- Juliet Sierra**

VFR Departure Scenario Two
– ATZ Departure with ATC

Frequencies: TOWER 132.75

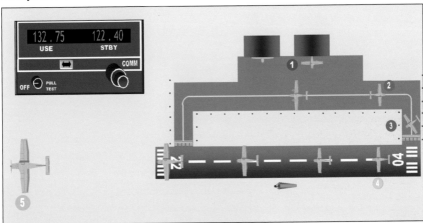

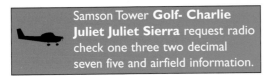

Samson Tower **Golf- Charlie Juliet Juliet Sierra** request radio check one three two decimal seven five and airfield information.

Golf- Charlie Juliet Juliet Sierra **Samson Tower** readability five, Runway zero four, surface wind zero seven zero eight knots, QNH niner niner four millibars, temperature minus two.

Readability five, runway zero four, QNH niner niner four millibars. Request taxi from hangar four **Golf- Charlie Juliet Juliet Sierra.**

Golf- Juliet Sierra taxi holding point Echo, follow the Seneca crossing right to left.

2

 After the Seneca taxi holding point Echo **Golf- Juliet Sierra**

 Golf- Juliet Sierra report ready for departure

 Wilco **Golf- Juliet Sierra**

3

 Golf- Juliet Sierra ready for departure.

 Golf- Juliet Sierra hold position, after the departing Seminole line up runway zero four.

 After the departing Seminole line up runway zero four **Golf- Juliet Sierra.**

Golf- Juliet Sierra after departure climb straight ahead to altitude two thousand feet before turning right. Cleared for take off, surface wind zero niner zero, niner knots

After departure climb straight ahead to altitude two thousand feet before turning right. Cleared for take off, **Golf- Juliet Sierra**

4

Golf- Juliet Sierra correct, report reaching altitude two thousand feet.

Wilco **Golf- Juliet Sierra**

Golf- Juliet Sierra level altitude two thousand feet

5

Golf- Juliet Sierra roger, freecall enroute frequency

Changing to Caskill Information one two two decimal four **Golf- Juliet Sierra**

Note: For VFR flights local departure instructions may be given with a take off clearance, this is to ensure that no conflictions exist with other aircraft operating in the vicinity of the aerodrome.

Left Intentionally Blank

Chapter 2 - Part 5

Aerodrome Traffic Circuit and Joining the Circuit

Typical left hand pattern

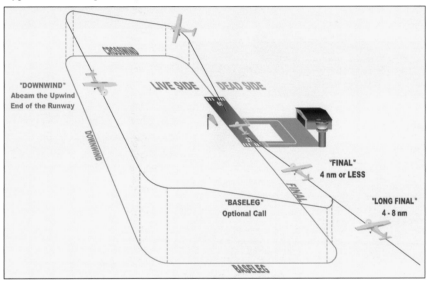

Requests to join the circuit should be made in sufficient time for a planned entry taking other traffic into account. Where an ATIS broadcast is established this should be listened to and receipt acknowledged on first contact with the aerodrome.

Where a right hand (non-standard) pattern is used it will be specified. A left hand pattern will not be specified unless the circuit direction is variable.

To Join the Circuit

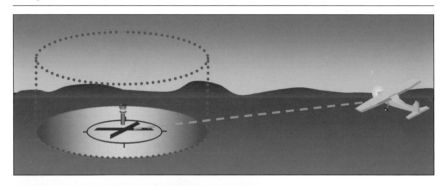

Norwich tower **Golf-Charlie Juliet Juliet Sierra**

Golf- Charlie Juliet Juliet Sierra **Norwich Tower** pass your message

Norwich Tower **Golf- Charlie Juliet Juliet Sierra** PA28 one zero miles south, altitude two thousand feet, request joining instructions

Golf- Juliet Sierra **Norwich Tower** join right-hand downwind runway two seven, circuit height one thousand feet QFE niner eight six millibars

Join right-hand downwind runway two seven height one thousand feet QFE niner eight six millibars **Golf- Juliet Sierra**

Where ATIS is available receipt of the information should be acknowledged on the initial call:

Coventry Tower **Golf- Charlie Juliet Juliet Sierra** PA28 one five miles south, altitude two thousand feet, information Romeo, request joining instructions.

Golf- Charlie Juliet Juliet Sierra **Coventry Tower** join right-hand downwind runway two three, Romeo current, QNH one zero zero four

Join right-hand downwind runway two three QNH one zero zero four **Golf- Juliet Sierra**

An alternative joining procedure often used at smaller aerodromes is the standard overhead join. In this case the aircraft is required to:

a.   Overfly the aerodrome at 2000ft above aerodrome elevation

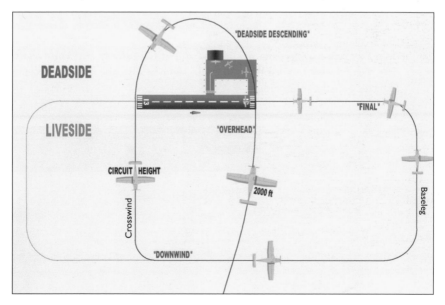

Golf- Juliet Sierra report
overhead for a standard
overhead join

Wilco **Golf- Juliet Sierra**

b. Determine the circuit direction if not already known *(signal square, windsock, other traffic)*

c. Descend on the **"dead side"** to circuit height:

Golf- Juliet Sierra
dead side descending

Golf- Juliet Sierra roger,
report downwind

Wilco **Golf- Juliet Sierra**

d. Join the circuit by crossing the upwind end of the runway at circuit height, it is a good idea to keep the runway in sight to one side and avoid flying directly over the threshold.

e. Position downwind

Golf- Juliet Sierra downwind

See diagram opposite.

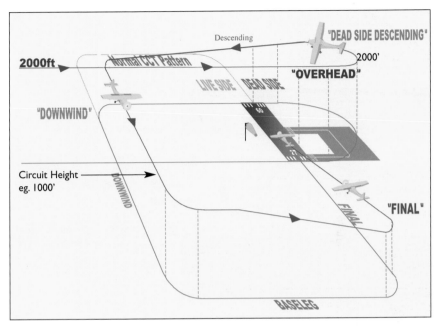

If the aircraft is arriving from a suitable direction and the prevailing traffic situation is favourable it may be possible to make a straight in approach:

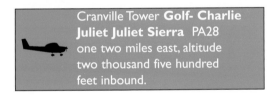

Cranville Tower **Golf- Charlie Juliet Juliet Sierra** PA28 one two miles east, altitude two thousand five hundred feet inbound.

Golf-Charlie Juliet Juliet Sierra **Cranville Tower** cleared straight in approach runway two seven, wind two two zero degrees niner knots, QNH one zero zero two. Report final.

Cleared straight in runway two seven QNH one zero zero two. Wilco **Golf- Juliet Sierra**

Having joined the circuit routine reports will need to be made as required by local procedures.

For Example:

 **Golf- Juliet Sierra** downwind

 Golf- Juliet Sierra report final number two, follow a Cessna 172 base leg

 Report final number two, visual with the C172 **Golf- Juliet Sierra**

 **Golf- Juliet Sierra** final

 Golf- Juliet Sierra continue approach runway two seven traffic to vacate

At aerodromes handling larger aircraft a vortex wake warning may also be issued:

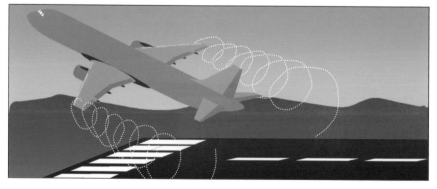

 **Golf- Juliet Sierra** downwind

 Golf- Juliet Sierra report final number two, follow a Boeing seven three seven one mile final caution vortex wake the recommended spacing six miles

 Report final number two, visual with the Boeing seven three seven **Golf- Juliet Sierra**

 Golf- Juliet Sierra final

 Golf- Juliet Sierra continue approach runway two seven traffic to vacate

It may be necessary in order to ensure a smooth flow of traffic to issue delaying or expediting instructions:

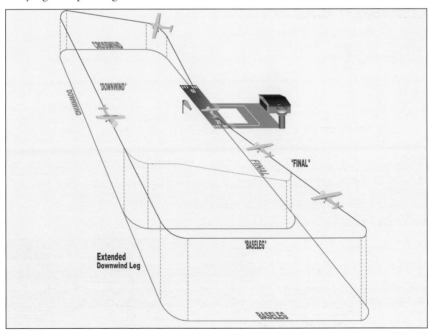

Golf- Juliet Sierra extend
downwind, number three, follow
Seneca four miles final

 Extend downwind, follow the
Seneca **Golf- Juliet Sierra**

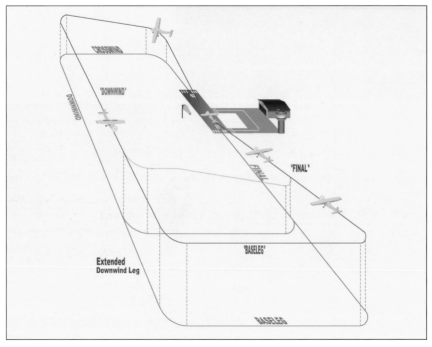

Or

 Golf- Juliet Sierra delaying action.
Orbit left report again downwind

 Orbit left, Wilco **Golf- Juliet
Sierra**

Orbit simply means make a 360° turn in the direction specified.

Chapter 2 - Part 6

Final Approach and Landing

A **"final"** report is made when an aircraft turns onto final approach. If the aircraft is established on the final approach track at a distance greater than four miles from touchdown a **"long final"** report is made.

There are a finite number of responses to be expected from the ATSU in reply:

- **Cleared to land**
- **Cleared touch and go**
- **Continue approach**
- **Land after**
- **Go around**
- **Land your discretion – at an AFIS station**

A clearance to land must be read back and any of the above options will often include the runway designator, and this should be acknowledged.

Golf- Juliet Sierra final

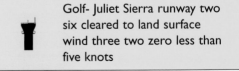
Golf- Juliet Sierra runway two six cleared to land surface wind three two zero less than five knots

Cleared to land
Golf- Juliet Sierra

During training if circuits are being flown touch and go landings may be requested:

 Golf- Juliet Sierra
downwind touch and go

 Golf- Juliet Sierra roger
report final

 Wilco **Golf- Juliet Sierra**

 Golf- Juliet Sierra final

 Golf- Juliet Sierra runway two
four cleared touch and go
surface wind calm

 Runway two four cleared touch
and go **Golf- Juliet Sierra**

Or

 Golf- Juliet Sierra unable to
approve due traffic full stop
landing. Runway two four
cleared to land surface wind calm

 Runway two four cleared to land
Golf- Juliet Sierra

It is helpful for traffic management if the controller is advised when an aircraft flying a series of circuits is on the last one. Suitable phraseology is:

Golf- Juliet Sierra downwind last landing

Or

Golf- Juliet Sierra downwind to land

"**Continue approach**" will be passed when it is not possible to issue landing clearance at the time, but it is expected that the runway will be unobstructed and available in good time for your aircraft to make a safe landing. If the response is to continue the controller may not explain why landing clearance has not been issued, but it must be emphasised that "continue" is not an invitation to land! The pilot must wait for landing clearance or missed approach instructions:

Air France eight eight seven final

Air France eight eight seven continue approach runway one four wind one zero zero, one eight knots.

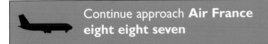

Continue approach **Air France eight eight seven**

Air France eight eight seven runway one four cleared to land wind one two zero degrees one five knots

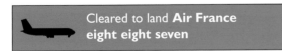

Cleared to land **Air France eight eight seven**

A preceding aircraft may have landed but not yet vacated the runway, in this scenario a following aircraft may be permitted to touchdown provided:

a.   The runway is long enough to allow safe separation and there is no evidence to suggest that the braking action may be adversely affected

b.   It is daylight

c.   The controller is satisfied that the landing aircraft will be able to see the preceding aircraft which has landed clearly and continuously until it has vacated the runway; and

d.   The pilot of the following aircraft is warned. Responsibility for ensuring safe separation rests with the pilot of the following aircraft.

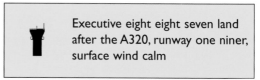

Executive eight eight seven land after the A320, runway one niner, surface wind calm

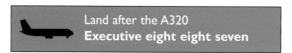

Land after the A320
Executive eight eight seven

To avoid an unsafe situation, the controller may instruct the pilot to initiate a missed approach. Transmissions will be kept brief due to the increase in cockpit workload:

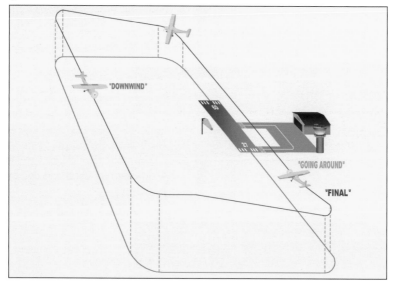

Ryanair eight eight seven go
around, I say again go around
acknowledge

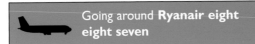

Going around **Ryanair eight
eight seven**

In the event of a missed approach VFR traffic is expected to continue into the normal traffic circuit, IFR traffic will carry out the published missed approach procedure, unless alternative instructions are issued.

If the pilot wishes to initiate a missed approach, as soon as practicable ATC should be advised:

Modernair eight eight seven
going around

Or

Modernair eight eight seven roger
standard missed approach

Modernair eight eight seven roger
climb straight ahead to altitude
two thousand feet.

Straight ahead to altitude two
thousand feet **Modernair eight
eight seven**

At an aerodrome with a Flight Information Service the phraseology is slightly different:

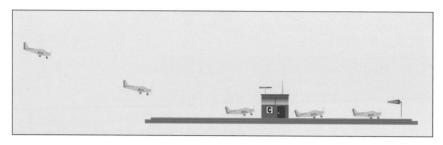

Golf- Juliet Sierra final

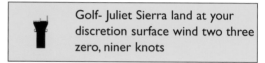

Golf- Juliet Sierra land at your discretion surface wind two three zero, niner knots

Landing **Golf- Juliet Sierra**

Or simply

Golf- Juliet Sierra

Alternatively:

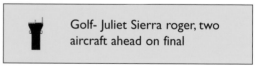

Golf- Juliet Sierra roger, two aircraft ahead on final

Roger **Golf- Juliet Sierra**

For training purposes the pilot may request permission to make an approach along, or parallel to the runway without landing:

Golf- Juliet Sierra request low approach runway three six for training

Golf- Juliet Sierra runway three six, cleared low approach not below four hundred feet above threshold elevation, vehicle on the runway.

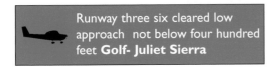

Runway three six cleared low approach not below four hundred feet **Golf- Juliet Sierra**

Visual Inspection

The pilot of a retractable undercarriage aircraft may request a fly past of the control tower for the purpose of a visual inspection of the landing gear from the ground. If the tower is located some way from the runway itself there may be a wait while a suitably qualified observer is positioned closer to the runway.

Golf- Juliet Sierra request low pass unsafe left gear indication.

Golf- Juliet Sierra runway three six cleared low pass not below four hundred feet report final

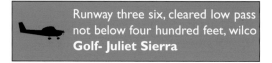

Runway three six, cleared low pass not below four hundred feet, wilco **Golf- Juliet Sierra**

If the purpose of the observation is for a landing gear check one of the following replies will be used to describe its condition:

* Landing gear appears down
* Right/left/nose wheel appears up (or down)
* Right/left/nose wheel does not appear up (or down)

Chapter 2 - Part 7

After Landing

Controllers will not pass taxi instructions until the landing roll is completed. At aerodromes where both a Tower and Ground frequency are in operation pilots should remain with the Tower until advised; this will usually be until the aircraft has vacated the runway.

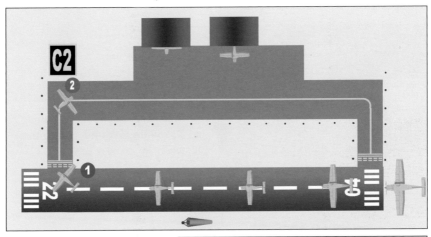

Example 1

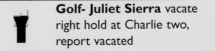

Golf- Juliet Sierra vacate right hold at Charlie two, report vacated

Vacate right, hold Charlie two, wilco **Golf- Juliet Sierra**

Golf- Juliet Sierra vacated

Or

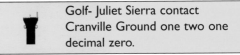

Golf- Juliet Sierra contact Cranville Ground one two one decimal zero.

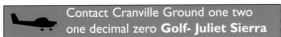

Contact Cranville Ground one two one decimal zero **Golf- Juliet Sierra**

Example 2

 Golf- Bravo Hotel vacate left, when vacated contact Cranville Ground one two one decimal zero

 Left and when vacated Cranville Ground one two one decimal zero **Golf- Bravo Hotel**

 Cranville Ground **Golf- Tango Alpha Bravo Hotel** runway vacated

 Golf- Tango Alpha Bravo Hotel **Cranville Ground**, taxi to the apron via taxiway Bravo

 Taxiway Bravo to the apron **Golf- Tango Alpha Bravo Hotel**

Chapter 2 - Part 8

VFR and Approach Control

Departures

A departing VFR flight being handled by approach control may be passed information on relevant known traffic; the pilot can then use this information to maintain his own separation. Pilots should advise the approach control unit when leaving the area under its jurisdiction.

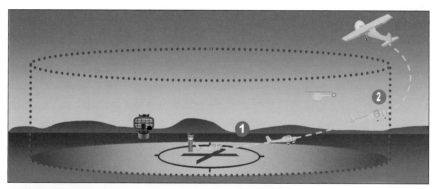

Birmingham Approach **Golf- Bravo November Oscar Zulu**

I

Golf- Bravo November Oscar Zulu **Birmingham Approach** traffic opposite direction R22 helicopter VFR altitude one thousand five hundred feet, report northern zone boundary.

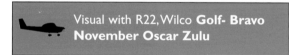

Visual with R22, Wilco **Golf- Bravo November Oscar Zulu**

2 **Golf-Bravo November Oscar Zulu** passing zone boundary

Golf-Oscar Zulu roger Flight information available from London Information one two four decimal six.

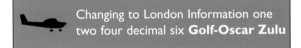

Changing to London Information one two four decimal six **Golf-Oscar Zulu**

Arrivals

Subject to local procedures, the pilot of an arriving VFR flight is required to establish contact with the approach control unit before entering the area under its jurisdiction i.e. before entering a control zone or ATZ. Where there is an ATIS broadcast the pilot should acknowledge receipt on initial contact, elsewhere the approach controller will pass the aerodrome information.

To reduce the chances of an aircraft's transmission interfering with another airfield using the same frequency, the UK CAA recommends the following maximum ranges for contacting an ATSU at an aerodrome:

At Major International Airports	
Tower	Up to 25nm and height 4000ft
Approach	Up to 25nm and height 10,000ft
At Other Airfields	
Tower, AFIS, A/G	Only within the immediate vicinity of the aerodrome, and heights below 1000ft
Approach control	Not more than 10nm from the airfield and not above height 3000ft

ATC's response to the initial contact call will either be **"go ahead"** *("pass your message" in the UK)* or **"standby"**, simply meaning that the controller is engaged with another task. You should say **nothing** in response to an instruction to **"standby"**, simply wait and the controller will call you. The controller will need to know certain details regarding your flight; to ensure that all the information is passed an aide-memoire is helpful, a widely used one is PHACER. Thus, following the aircraft **callsign** and type:

P	–	Point of departure and present position
H	–	Heading
A	–	Altitude
C	–	Conditions VFR/IFR
E	–	Estimate, or en-route from departure aerodrome to destination
R	–	Request

VFR Arrival Scenario 1 *(Control Zone)*

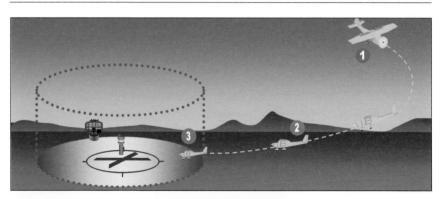

Bournemouth Approach **Golf- Oscar Hotel Echo Echo,** information Juliet QNH one zero zero two.

Golf- Oscar Hotel Echo Echo
Bournemouth Approach
Juliet current, QNH correct,
pass your message

Golf- Oscar Hotel Echo Echo PA28

P – from Newcastle, overhead Popham
H – heading two two zero
A – altitude two thousand feet QNH
one zero zero two
C – VFR
E – ETA one four
R – request joining instructions

(2)

Golf- Oscar Hotel Echo Echo
cleared from the zone boundary
VFR not above altitude two
thousand feet QNH one zero
zero two report aerodrome
in sight

Cleared to enter the control zone VFR
not above altitude two thousand feet
QNH one zero zero two, Wilco
Golf- Oscar Hotel Echo Echo

Golf-Echo Echo traffic is a
Tomahawk northbound from
Bournemouth estimating the zone
boundary at zero seven

Golf- Echo Echo visual

 Aerodrome in sight **Golf- Echo Echo**

 Golf- Echo Echo join right base runway two six

 Join right base runway two six **Golf- Echo Echo**

 Golf- Echo Echo contact Bournemouth Tower one two five decimal six

 Contact Bournemouth Tower one two five decimal six **Golf- Echo Echo**

Arrival Scenario 2 *(ATZ with ATC)*

Where just an ATZ is established around an aerodrome, the callsign used by the ground station will give you a clue as to level of service to be expected. *see p23.* During your pre-flight planning checking either the AIP or Flight Guide will give you the callsign of the ground station next to the appropriate frequency.

c/s Cranfield.   APP 122.85   TWR 134.925   Dep ATIS 121.875

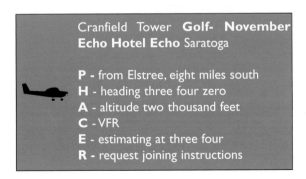

Cranfield Tower **Golf- November Echo Hotel Echo** Saratoga

P - from Elstree, eight miles south
H - heading three four zero
A - altitude two thousand feet
C - VFR
E - estimating at three four
R - request joining instructions

Golf- November Echo Hotel Echo Cranfield Tower join left base runway two two, QFE niner niner two millibars, report airfield in sight.

Join left base runway two two, QFE niner niner two millibars, wilco **Golf- November Echo Hotel Echo**

Field in sight **Golf- November Echo Hotel Echo**

Golf- Hotel Echo report left base runway two two.

Wilco **Golf- Hotel Echo**

Left base **Golf- Hotel Echo**

Golf- Hotel Echo roger, report final runway two two, number two to an AA5 two mile final.

Report final runway two two, visual with the AA5 **Golf- Hotel Echo**

Golf- Hotel Echo final

Golf- Hotel Echo runway two two, cleared to land surface wind one seven zero degrees eight knots.

Runway two two Cleared to land **Golf- Hotel Echo**

VFR Arrival Scenario 3 *(ATZ with Aerodrome Flight Information Service)*

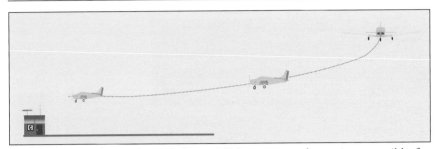

It should be emphasised that a FISO at an aerodrome is responsible for providing information useful for the safe and efficient operation of traffic **at the aerodrome or within its associated ATZ.**

Duxford Information **Golf- Golf Oscar Kilo Bravo**

Golf- Golf Oscar Kilo Bravo, Duxford Information pass your message

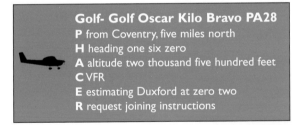

Golf- Golf Oscar Kilo Bravo PA28
P from Coventry, five miles north
H heading one six zero
A altitude two thousand five hundred feet
C VFR
E estimating Duxford at zero two
R request joining instructions

Golf- Kilo Bravo, overhead join runway two three, QNH one zero two four QFE one zero two zero, two aircraft in the circuit

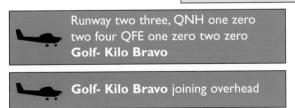

Runway two three, QNH one zero two four QFE one zero two zero **Golf- Kilo Bravo**

Golf- Kilo Bravo joining overhead

Golf- Kilo Bravo, report downwind, a Cherokee late downwind.

 Wilco **Golf- Kilo Bravo**

Golf- Kilo Bravo downwind

 Golf- Kilo Bravo report final runway two two, Cherokee one mile final.

Wilco **Golf- Kilo Bravo**

Golf- Kilo Bravo final two two

 Golf- Kilo Bravo runway two two, land your discretion surface wind two three zero, one seven

 **Golf- Kilo Bravo**

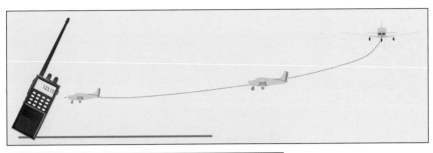

 Fowlmere Radio **Golf- Oscar Sierra Mike Golf**

 Golf- Oscar Sierra Mike Golf **Fowlmere Radio**

 Golf- Oscar Sierra Mike Golf, inbound request airfield information

 Golf- Mike Golf runway two five right hand circuit, QFE one zero three two.

 Right-hand circuit, QFE one zero three two **Golf- Mike Golf**

 Golf- Mike Golf downwind right hand two five.

 Golf- Mike Golf roger

 Golf- Mike Golf final runway two five.

 Golf- Mike Golf roger

Left Intentionally Blank

Chapter 2 - Part 9

Special VFR Operations

Special VFR clearances are only permitted within control ZONES, usually at the request of the pilot. SVFR is a concession offered by ATC, which allows an aircraft to operate **within a control zone which is Class A** or in any other control zone in **IMC or at night**, without requiring compliance with the Instrument Flight Rules.

When flying on a SVFR clearance the pilot:

*   Must comply with ATC instructions
*   Is responsible for ensuring that his flight conditions enable him to remain clear of cloud and obstructions and determine his flight path with reference to the surface
*   Is responsible for flying within the limitations of his licence
*   Is responsible for complying with the relevant low flying restrictions of Rule 5 *(although the 1500ft rule does not apply, the need to "alight clear" is always applicable)*
*   Is responsible for avoiding aerodrome traffic zones unless prior permission to enter has been obtained from the appropriate ATSU.

No separation will be provided between SVFR flights flying in notified areas or routes where an individual clearance is not required, or between aircraft using such areas or routes and other flights on SVFR clearances. Otherwise standard separation is applied between SVFR flights and between SVFR and IFR flights. SVFR aircraft are not normally given a specific height to fly; controllers achieve vertical separation from higher traffic by requiring the SVFR flight to fly not above a specific level.

A full flight plan is not necessary for a SVFR flight, however brief details should be passed by the pilot including the **callsign, aircraft type and pilot's intentions, including for inbound aircraft, an ETA for zone entry.**

Zone Departure Clearance

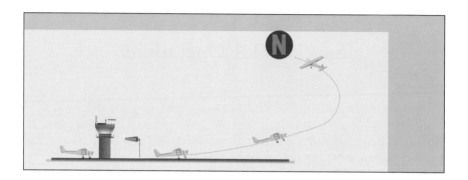

Golf- Charlie Juliet Juliet Sierra leave the control zone special VFR via route November, not above altitude three thousand feet, squawk three four four five.

Leave the control zone special VFR via route November, not above altitude three thousand feet, squawk three four four five **Golf- Charlie Juliet Juliet Sierra**

Golf-Juliet Sierra correct.

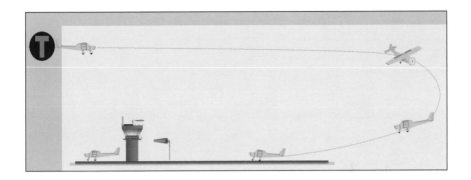

 Golf-Mike Oscar Mike Oscar enter the control zone special VFR not above altitude two thousand feet via reporting point Tango, squawk three four four five

 Enter the control zone special VFR not above altitude two thousand feet via reporting point Tango, squawk three four four five **Golf-Mike Oscar Mike Oscar**

Zone Transit

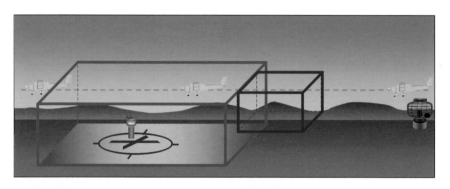

 Luton Radar **Golf- Charlie Juliet Juliet Sierra**

 Golf- Charlie Juliet Juliet Sierra **Luton Radar** pass your message

Golf- Charlie Juliet Juliet Sierra PA28 request SVFR zone transit ETA zone boundary four three

 Golf- Charlie Juliet Juliet Sierra transit the control zone special VFR not above two thousand feet route via the aerodrome overhead, squawk three four four five.

 Transit the control zone special VFR not above two thousand feet route via the aerodrome overhead, squawk three four four five **Golf- Charlie Juliet Juliet Sierra**

The details required to be passed in order to obtain a SVFR clearance are:

C	–	Callsign
T	–	Type
I	–	Intentions
E	–	ETA

Left Intentionally Blank

Chapter 2 - Part 10

Essential Aerodrome Information

Essential aerodrome information is that concerning the condition of the manoeuvring area and its associated facilities, which may constitute a hazard to a particular aircraft. It will be passed to pilots prior to start up and taxi or prior to the aircraft commencing its final approach, in sufficient time to ensure the safe operation of aircraft. If the aerodrome has an ATIS facility essential information may be appended to the broadcast.

Items include:

- Construction or maintenance work on or adjacent to the manoeuvring area
- Rough or broken surfaces on runways or taxiways, and whether the areas are marked or not
- Snow and ice on runways
- Water on runways
- Snow banks or drifts adjacent to a runway or taxiway
- Other temporary hazards including parked aircraft, aircraft engaged in engine ground running and any bird activity
- Failure or irregular operation of approach aids or the aerodrome lighting system

 Modernair one two zero caution work in progress on the main apron centreline.

 Modernair one two zero caution work in progress south side of taxiway Alpha.

 Modernair one two zero runway surface damp, wet, wet.

Modernair one two zero caution approach lighting runway two six unserviceable.

 Modernair one two zero caution large flock of birds observed at the Delta intersection.

 Modernair one two zero caution as you pass abeam stand 3 F27 to your right has started engines.

 Roger **Modernair one two zero.**

Chapter 2 - Part 11

Reproduced from CAP 413
FISO Phraseology

Taxi Instructions prior to take off, after landing and other ground movement.

(Aircraft Callsign) taxi holding point *(designation)* runway *(designation)* via *(route)*, surface wind *(number)* degrees *(number)* knots, QNH/QFE *(pressure)* millibars, left/right hand circuit.

(Aircraft Callsign) taxi to stand *(designation)* via *(route)*.

(Aircraft Callsign) taxi to *(location)*.

When necessary, detailed taxying instruction e.g. turn left from the apron and take the first intersection right.

(Aircraft Callsign) after the *(aircraft type)* passing *(e.g. left to right)* taxi holding point *(designation)* runway *(designation)* surface wind *(number)* degrees *(number)* knots, QNH/QFE *(pressure)* millibars, left/right hand circuit.

(Aircraft Callsign) follow the *(aircraft type)* passing *(eg. left to right)*

(Aircraft Callsign) hold Position.

Note: FISOs are permitted to pass instructions to helicopters engaged in air taxiing. However, when the pilot reports ready to lift and depart, the FISO shall pass information. For all inbound helicopters, information shall be passed until they land or reach the hover prior to air taxiing to the parking area. Thereafter, instructions shall be given until the helicopter lands.

Aircraft at the holding point of runway to be used for departure ready for take-off ****Note:** Pilots will notify the FISO of their intentions.	*(Aircraft Callsign)* hold position. *(Aircraft Callsign)* **take off at your discretion**, surface wind *(number)* degrees *(number)* knots. *(Aircraft Callsign)* traffic is *(traffic information)* **take off at your discretion**, surface wind *(number)* degrees *(number)* knots. **
Aircraft at the holding point of runway to be used for departure ready for take-off with the possibility of requiring a backtrack ****Note:** Pilots will notify the FISO of their intentions.	*(Aircraft Callsign)* do you require to backtrack the runway?**
Aircraft requiring a backtrack ****Note:** Pilots will notify the FISO of their intentions.	*(Aircraft Callsign)* report entering the runway. *(Aircraft Callsign)* report lining up. ** *(Aircraft Callsign)* traffic is *(traffic information)* report entering the runway and lining up. ** *(Aircraft Callsign)* the *(aircraft type)* has landed to vacate the there is a *(aircraft type)* on a 2 mile final. Report lining up. ** *(Aircraft Callsign)* backtrack as required, surface wind *(number)* degrees *(number)* knots, take off at your discretion.**

Instructions for crossing runway in use *Note:* 'Report vacated' instructions may be omitted when the FISO has continuous sight of the vehicle or aircraft crossing.	*(Aircraft Callsign)* cross runway *(designation)* at *(point of crossing)*, Report vacated. * *(Aircraft Callsign)* cross, report vacated.*
When Airborne	*(Aircraft Callsign)* roger, report (downwind or position).
Aircraft wishes to transit the ATZ	*(Aircraft Callsign) (traffic and aerodrome information)*, report entering/overhead/leaving.
Aircraft wishes to enter the ATZ for landing	*(Aircraft Callsign)* runway *(designation)* left/right hand circuit, surface wind *(number)* degrees *(number)* knots, QNH/QFE *(traffic information and essential aerodrome information as appropriate)*.
Aircraft reports joining the circuit	*(Aircraft Callsign)* roger, *(traffic information)* report downwind/ base/final. *(If number 1 and runway is clear) (Aircraft Callsign)* land/touch and go at your discretion, surface wind *(number)* degrees *(number)* knots or *(if aircraft has traffic ahead on final) (Aircraft Callsign)* roger, *(number)* aircraft ahead on final or *(if the runway is occupied) (Aircraft Callsign)* the runway is occupied *(traffic information)*.
Aircraft expects Air Traffic Control Service	*(Aircraft Callsign)* no ATC Service available. Flight Information Service only.

Air-Ground Communication Service Operator Phraseology

Event	Response
Aircraft Ready to Taxi	*(Aircraft Callsign)* runway *(designation)* left/right hand circuit QFE/QNH *(pressure)* millibars.
Aircraft wishes to Cross a Runway	*(Aircraft Callsign)* (traffic information eg. I have no known traffic, or, after *(aircraft type)*, has landed I have no known traffic).
Aircraft Ready to Take Off	*(Aircraft Callsign)* no known traffic *(or traffic information)* surface wind *(number)* degrees *(number)* knots.
Aircraft Reports Airborne	*(Aircraft Callsign)* roger.
Aircraft Overflying Reports Entering ATZ or asks for Traffic Information	*(Aircraft Callsign) (traffic information) (aerodrome information).*
Aircraft Requests Joining Information for a Landing	*(Aircraft Callsign)* runway *(designation)* surface wind *(number)* degrees *(number)* knots, QFE/QNH *(pressure)* millibars *(traffic information).*
Aircraft Reports Joining Circuit	*(Aircraft Callsign)* roger, *(plus, when applicable, updated traffic information and any changes to aerodrome information).*
Aircraft Reports Landed and/or Runway Vacated	*(Aircraft Callsign) (any appropriate aerodrome information).*
Note: Air ground operators must not use the expression '**at your discretion**' as this is associated with the service provided by FISOs and is likely to cause confusion to pilots.	

1. What is the meaning of Readability 3 and Readability 5?

2. What is the correct phraseology to use when you are ready for take off?

3. What service provides automated aerodrome information and met conditions?

4. When may the phrase **"take off"** be used by a pilot?

5. What details must be passed to obtain a SVFR clearance?

6. What does the phrase **"go around"** mean and what should your response be?

7. What is the definition of a SVFR flight?

8. At what range would you report **"long final"**?

9. What does Flight Information Service at an aerodrome provide?

10. What should your response be to an AFIS transmission **"land your discretion, surface wind 090 12"**?

11. What should your response be to an instruction to **"standby"**?

Left Intentionally Blank

Chapter 3

En-route Procedures

Left Intentionally Blank

Chapter 3 - Part 1

En-route Procedures - Introduction

There are various levels of service available to en-route aircraft.

Radar Services

Radar services comprise:

a. **Separation** of arriving, departing and en-route traffic
b. Radar **vectoring**
c. **Position information** to assist in navigation
d. Assistance to aircraft crossing controlled airspace

Within controlled airspace (Class A to E) a Radar Control Service will be provided. Outside controlled airspace (Class F and G) a Lower Airspace Radar Service may be available, comprising of either a Radar Advisory Service or a Radar Information Service, the former being more suitable for IFR operations, the latter for VFR.

Procedural Services

Should radar not be available traffic must be separated either vertically, or horizontally using either distance or time. This requires regular position reports from pilots to ensure that the traffic situation is up to date. The standard format for a position report is:

A	–	aircraft callsign
P	–	position
T	–	time
L	–	level
N	–	next reporting point
E	–	ETA for the next reporting point

Information Service

An information service is available from certain ATSUs, providing pilots with data useful for the safe and efficient conduct of flights. London and Scottish Information and flight information service (**FIS**) units at aerodromes all provide this service. It should be noted that London & Scottish Information provide information only and have no control function.

Alerting Service

An alerting service is provided to notify appropriate organisations regarding aircraft in need of search and rescue aid. All ATSUs automatically provide this service to any aircraft known to them.

Chapter 3 - Part 2

General Radar Phraseology

The following is an overview of general radar phraseology commonly used in communications between aircraft and all types of radar unit. Usually the callsign suffix used by a unit is sufficient to determine its function.

In a radar environment all heading information given by the pilot or instructions issued by controllers are in degrees magnetic.

The phrase **"under radar control"** will only be used when a radar control service is being provided. ie. within controlled airspace.

Primary Radar Identification

When operating using primary radar all the controller will have to represent your aircraft on the screen is a **"blip"**, looking remarkably similar to all the other blips!

Before any type of radar service is provided the controller must identify the aircraft concerned. It must be noted that **the act of identifying an aircraft is not a service** in itself and a pilot should not assume that he is receiving a radar service, especially when flying outside controlled airspace, unless the controller specifically states that this is the case.

There are four methods used to achieve identification:

a.   **The Turn Method:** the aircraft's heading is ascertained and after the track has been observed the pilot is instructed to make a heading change of at least 30°

b.   **Departing Aircraft Method:** correlation of a radar return with a known departure time

c.   **Position Report Method:** correlating a radar return with a report from the pilot that the aircraft is over either:
     i.   An exact reporting point
     ii.   A radial and DME from a co-located VOR/DME
     iii. Over a visual reference point or prominent geographical location

d.   **SSR Information**

 Golf- Juliet Sierra report heading

 Heading two five zero
Golf- Juliet Sierra

 Golf- Juliet Sierra
for identification
turn left heading two two zero

 Left heading two two zero
Golf- Juliet Sierra

 Golf- Juliet Sierra identified one five miles north east of Luton, Radar Information service.

 Radar Information service
Golf- Juliet Sierra

Or   Golf- Juliet Sierra not identified. Resume own navigation.

 Wilco **Golf- Juliet Sierra**

You will be advised if the identification of your aircraft is lost, or about to be lost, and appropriate instructions given.

Example 1

Golf-India Golf Oscar Romeo radar identification lost due radar failure. Resume own navigation. Flight information available from London Information one two four decimal six

Changing to London Information one two four decimal six
Golf-India Golf Oscar Romeo

Example 2

Modernair three three seven shortly leaving radar cover, radar service terminated squawk seven thousand. Report changing to enroute frequency.

Squawk seven thousand, radar service terminated, changing to Birmingham Approach one one eight decimal zero five
Modernair three three seven

Modernair three three seven, roger.

When a controller has identified an aircraft s/he will inform the pilot of the following:

a.   That the Aircraft is Identified, and
b.   The Position of the Aircraft

According to the circumstances below:

Method of Identification	Aircraft Flying Inside Controlled Airspace		Aircraft Flying Outside Controlled Airspace	
	Inform Identified	Pass Position	Inform Identified	Pass Position
Turn	Yes	Yes	Yes	Yes
Departing Aircraft	No	No	Yes	No
Position Report	No	No	Yes	No
SSR	No	No	Yes	Yes

Radar Vectoring

A controller has complete freedom to instruct an aircraft to turn in any direction, however when avoiding unknown traffic the rules of the air will be observed if practicable.

Aircraft may be given specific vectors to fly in order to establish lateral separation; the reason for requiring a particular vector to be maintained may be given.

Example 1

Speedbird four seven seven turn left heading one two zero for separation

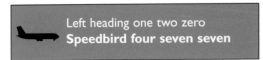

Left heading one two zero
Speedbird four seven seven

Example 2

Shamrock four seven seven turn right heading zero five zero, delaying action.

Right heading zero five zero
Shamrock four seven seven

Sometimes an aircraft's heading is ascertained and, once known, separation can be achieved by requiring the aircraft to continue on its existing heading.

Golf- Juliet Sierra continue present heading and report that heading

Heading three four zero
Golf- Juliet Sierra

Or the controller may require an aircraft to fly a particular heading:

Golf- Juliet Sierra fly heading zero niner zero

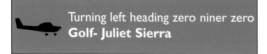
Turning left heading zero niner zero
Golf- Juliet Sierra

Once vectoring is complete the pilot will be given position information and if necessary appropriate instructions before being instructed to resume his own navigation.

Example 1

Golf-Hotel Hotel resume
own navigation direct Bovingdon
position is five miles south
of Luton

Direct Bovingdon
Golf-Hotel Hotel

Example 2

Golf-Charlie Sierra resume own
navigation direct Bovingdon track
two two zero magnetic, range
one two miles

Direct Bovingdon
Golf-Charlie Sierra

Example 3

Golf-Mike Oscar resume own
navigation, position is one five
miles southwest of Bovingdon

Wilco,
Golf-Mike Oscar

Occasionally an aircraft may be instructed to orbit (a complete turn of 360°) usually for delaying purposes or to achieve the required spacing behind preceding traffic.

Example 1

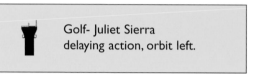

Golf- Juliet Sierra
delaying action, orbit left.

Orbit left **Golf- Juliet Sierra**

Example 2

Golf- Juliet Sierra delaying
action, make a three sixty
degree turn right

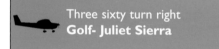

Three sixty turn right
Golf- Juliet Sierra

Left Intentionally Blank

Traffic Information & Traffic Avoidance

Traffic information will include the following:

a.   Bearing from the aircraft in terms of the 12 hour clock
b.   Distance from the aircraft in miles
c.   Direction in which the conflicting traffic is proceeding
d.   Level information when available, this may include unverified
      mode C readouts of unknown aircraft
e.   The relative speed of the conflicting traffic or type of aircraft may be
      included if known

Relative movement will be described by using one of the
following terms as applicable:

- **Closing**
- **Converging**
- **Parallel**
- **Same direction**
- **Opposite direction**
- **Diverging**
- **Overtaking**
- **Crossing left to right**
- **Crossing right to left**

Golf- Juliet Sierra unknown traffic two o'clock four miles opposite direction fast moving

Looking **Golf- Juliet Sierra**

Or

Traffic in sight **Golf- Juliet Sierra**

If the aircraft is receiving a **Radar Advisory Service** *(available to aircraft flying IFR)* vectors may be offered or requested by the pilot. The pilot will be advised when the conflict no longer exists.

Example 1

Golf- Juliet Sierra unknown traffic two o'clock four miles opposite direction fast moving. If not sighted turn left heading two four five

Turning left heading two four five
Golf- Juliet Sierra

Example 2

Modernair eight eight six unknown traffic ten o'clock eight miles crossing left to right, no height information

Modernair eight eight six
negative contact, request vectors

Modernair eight eight six turn right heading zero four five

Right heading zero four five
Modernair eight eight six

Modernair eight eight six clear of traffic, resume own navigation direct Barkway

Direct Barkway
Modernair eight eight six

Secondary Surveillance Radar (SSR) Procedures

The following phrases are instructions given by ATC to pilots regarding the operation of SSR transponders. The assignment of a code does not mean that a radar service is being provided. **SSR operating instructions require a readback.**

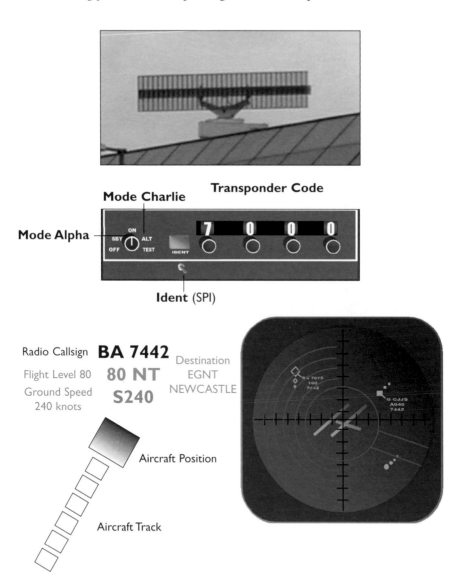

Mode Charlie

Transponder Code

Mode Alpha

Ident (SPI)

Radio Callsign **BA 7442**

Flight Level 80 **80 NT**

Ground Speed **S240**
240 knots

Destination
EGNT
NEWCASTLE

Aircraft Position

Aircraft Track

Phrase	Meaning
Squawk (Code)	Set the Mode A as instructed
Confirm Squawk	Confirm Mode & Code Set on the Transponder
Reset (Mode) (Code)	Reselect Assignment Mode & Code
Squawk Ident	Operate the SPI feature *(SPI = Special Position Identification)*
Squawk Mayday	Select Emergency
Squawk Standby	Select the Standby feature
Squawk Charlie	Select Altitude Reporting feature
Check Altimeter Setting & Report your Level	Check Pressure Setting & Report your Level
Stop Squawk Charlie, Wrong Indication	Deselect Pressure Altitude Reporting Transmission as the Indication is Faulty
Stop Squawk Charlie	Deselect Altitude Reporting
* **Verify your Level**	Check & Confirm your Level

* Used to Verify the Accuracy of the Mode C Level
Information displayed to Controller

Certain special purpose codes are in use and are listed below:

- **Mode A 7700:** Emergency
- **Mode A 7600:** Communications failure
- **Mode A 7500:** Unlawful interference *(hijack)*
- **Mode A 2000:** Entering the UK FIR from an adjacent region where the operation of transponders has not been required.

Additionally:

- **Mode A 7000:** Conspicuity code together with Mode C should be displayed by all suitably equipped aircraft unless:

    a.   They have been assigned a discrete code by an ATCU
    b.   They are flying in the aerodrome pattern below 3000 feet, or
    c.   They are transponding one of the special purpose codes listed above

Subject to the above, pilots are required to squawk 7000 when operating at FL100 and above and are advised to do so when operating below FL100.

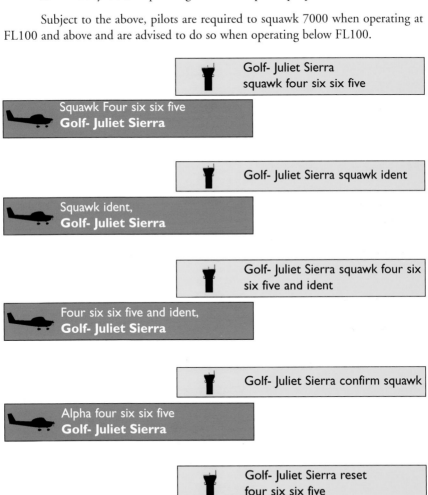

Golf- Juliet Sierra
squawk four six six five

Squawk Four six six five
Golf- Juliet Sierra

Golf- Juliet Sierra squawk ident

Squawk ident,
Golf- Juliet Sierra

Golf- Juliet Sierra squawk four six six five and ident

Four six six five and ident,
Golf- Juliet Sierra

Golf- Juliet Sierra confirm squawk

Alpha four six six five
Golf- Juliet Sierra

Golf- Juliet Sierra reset four six six five

Reset four six six five
Golf- Juliet Sierra

Golf- Juliet Sierra check altimeter setting and confirm level

 One zero one three, flight level five zero **Golf- Juliet Sierra**

 Golf- Juliet Sierra squawk Charlie

 Unable to comply, negative Mode Charlie **Golf- Juliet Sierra**

Chapter 3 - Part 4

Lower Airspace Radar Service (LARS)

The Lower Airspace Radar Service is available to all pilots flying in UK uncontrolled airspace up to and including FL95, within approximately 30nm of each participating ATSU. It is a discretionary service, subject mainly to the workload of the controller's primary task, and depending on the hours of operation of the particular unit may be available either H24 or solely during the opening times notified in the UKAIP. If following three consecutive calls no reply is received it can be assumed that the station is not operating.

Participating ATCUs are able to provide either a **Radar Advisory** or a **Radar Information Service**; both are available at the request of the pilot. The controller will inform pilots when they are receiving either a radar control (provided within controlled airspace), radar advisory or radar information service (provided outside controlled airspace); and also whenever the level of service changes.

Radar Advisory Service (RAS)	
Flight Rules	**IFR**
Provides	Traffic Information *(bearing, distance and, if known, level)* Avoiding action *(to achieve specified separation)*.
Note	Controllers will expect pilots to accept levels and vectors that may require flight in IMC.

Radar Information Service (RIS)	
Flight rules	**VFR or IFR**
Provides	Traffic Information only *(bearing, distance and, if known, level).*
Note	Vectors may be provided for tactical planning, but NOT to achieve separation. If a pilot requests avoiding action the controller will treat this as a request for a change in radar service i.e. a request for RAS.

Requesting a LARS

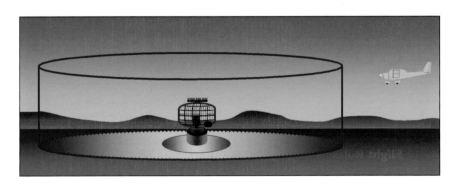

The type of service requested should be included in the initial contact transmission.

Birmingham Approach
Golf- Charlie Juliet Juliet Sierra
request Radar Information Service

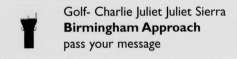

Golf- Charlie Juliet Juliet Sierra
Birmingham Approach
pass your message

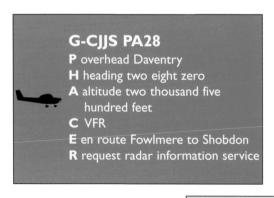

G-CJJS PA28
P overhead Daventry
H heading two eight zero
A altitude two thousand five
   hundred feet
C VFR
E en route Fowlmere to Shobdon
R request radar information service

Golf- Juliet Sierra roger, squawk
two three three four

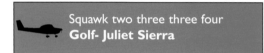

Squawk two three three four
Golf- Juliet Sierra

Golf- Juliet Sierra identified two
miles west of Daventry, Radar
Information Service

Radar Information
Golf- Juliet Sierra

Note: The type of radar service being provided is an item that must be readback.

Limiting a Service

Controllers will inform pilots when they limit a service and ensure the pilot understands the implications of the limitation. In particular the service will be limited when:

a. The aircraft is within 10 miles of the edge of the radar display, weather clutter or permanent echoes
b. The aircraft is operating in an area of high traffic density
c. The aircraft is operating near to the limits of radar cover, or
d. The service is provided using SSR only

Golf- Juliet Sierra limited Radar Information you are approaching an area of weather clutter, late notice of traffic from your left

Limited Radar Information
Golf- Juliet Sierra

Traffic Information

Golf- Juliet Sierra unknown traffic right two o'clock range five miles crossing right to left no height information

Roger **Golf- Juliet Sierra**

Or

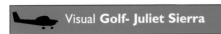

Visual **Golf- Juliet Sierra**

The phrase "pop-up" traffic may be used, this means that the traffic has suddenly appeared on the radar screen, perhaps climbing up from low level.

Traffic Avoidance

Provided only under a Radar Advisory Service:

Golf- Juliet Sierra Pop-up traffic right two o'clock seven miles crossing right to left, fast moving. If not sighted turn left heading two three zero

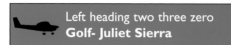

Left heading two three zero
Golf- Juliet Sierra

Golf- Juliet Sierra clear of traffic resume own navigation for Turweston, position is five miles south of Stratford

Wilco
Golf- Juliet Sierra

Change of Service

RAS and RIS are available outside controlled airspace. Within controlled airspace a **Radar Control Service** will be provided, this service is available to aircraft flying under IFR, special VFR or VFR, controllers will issue instructions to which:

a. Pilots of aircraft operating IFR are required to comply
b. Pilots of aircraft operating SVFR or VFR will comply unless they advise the controller otherwise

As you cross controlled airspace boundaries the controller will advise you that the service you are receiving has changed.

The phrase **"under radar control"** will only be used when a radar control service is being provided.

Golf- Juliet Sierra crossing the control zone boundary, Radar Control Service

Radar Control
Golf- Juliet Sierra

Golf- Juliet Sierra leaving the control zone Radar Information.

Radar Information
Golf- Juliet Sierra

Termination of Service

Golf- Juliet Sierra shortly leaving my radar cover, position is three zero miles west of Daventry. Radar service terminated, squawk seven thousand, report changing to enroute frequency.

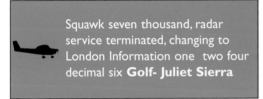

Squawk seven thousand, radar service terminated, changing to London Information one two four decimal six **Golf- Juliet Sierra**

Chapter 3 - Part 5

Radar Assistance to Aircraft with Radio Communication Failure

Radio communication failure is considered in greater detail in Chapter 4.

When a controller suspects that an aircraft has suffered a transmitter failure but is still able to receive messages, radar may be used to confirm that this is indeed the case. Subsequent instructions will be passed slowly and clearly and may be repeated.

Golf- Juliet Sierra reply not received. If you read **Bournemouth** turn left heading one two zero, I say again turn left heading one two zero

Golf- Juliet Sierra turn observed I will continue to pass instructions

Or

Golf- Juliet Sierra reply not received. If you read **Bournemouth** squawk ident, I say again squawk ident

Golf- Juliet Sierra ident observed, I will continue to pass instructions

Left Intentionally Blank

Chapter 3 - Part 6

MATZ Penetration

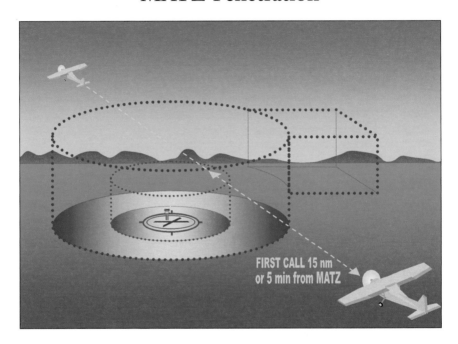

FIRST CALL 15 nm
or 5 min from MATZ

A Military Aerodrome Traffic Zone is a cylindrical column of airspace 5nm in radius extending from the surface to a height of 3000ft. One or more rectangular stubs may be present aligned with the approach path/s to the main runway/s, these stubs measure 5nm by 4nm and extend from a height of 1000ft to 3000ft. Outside published operating hours if no reply is received after two consecutive calls pilots may fly through the MATZ with caution. Contained within the MATZ is a normal ATZ, the rules for an ATZ apply within this airspace at all times.

Civilian traffic wishing to penetrate a MATZ should make contact with the military controller **15nm or 5 minutes** flying time before reaching the zone boundary, whichever is sooner.

Where two or more MATZs are close together one unit will be nominated as the CLUTCH MATZ. Within a MATZ vertical position is normally controlled by reference to QFE, if zones are contiguous the **"clutch QFE"** will be used, i.e the QFE at the unit in charge.

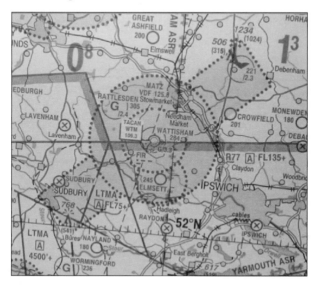

The major difference in phraseology is that on the initial call to the military controller the phrase **"Request MATZ penetration"** must be used.

Cottesmore Zone **Golf- Charlie Juliet Juliet Sierra** request MATZ penetration

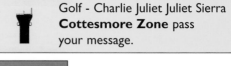

Golf - Charlie Juliet Juliet Sierra **Cottesmore Zone** pass your message.

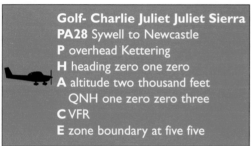

Golf- Charlie Juliet Juliet Sierra
PA28 Sywell to Newcastle
P overhead Kettering
H heading zero one zero
A altitude two thousand feet
   QNH one zero zero three
C VFR
E zone boundary at five five

Golf- Juliet Sierra squawk zero four five six

 Squawk zero four five six
Golf- Juliet Sierra

 Golf- Juliet Sierra identified. MATZ penetration approved at two thousand feet QFE one thousand. Report entering the MATZ

 MATZ penetration approved at two thousand feet QFE one thousand, Wilco **Golf- Juliet Sierra**

 Golf- Juliet Sierra entering MATZ

 Golf- Juliet Sierra roger report leaving the MATZ

 Wilco. **Golf- Juliet Sierra**

 Golf- Juliet Sierra leaving MATZ

 Golf- Juliet Sierra roger, squawk seven thousand, report changing to enroute frequency

 Squawk seven thousand, changing to London Information one two four decimal six **Golf- Juliet Sierra**

Left Intentionally Blank

Chapter 3 - Part 7

VHF Direction Finding (VDF)

VDF can be obtained from various aerodromes; these are listed in the UK AIP and detailed on aeronautical charts.

Although VDF may seem old fashioned it is in fact quite accurate, considering the overall accuracy of a VOR system is +/- 6° a Class A VDF bearing is three times as accurate.

Bearings are requested using the appropriate Q-code:

> **QDM**   **Magnetic Heading** to be steered by the aircraft to reach the station (assuming no wind)

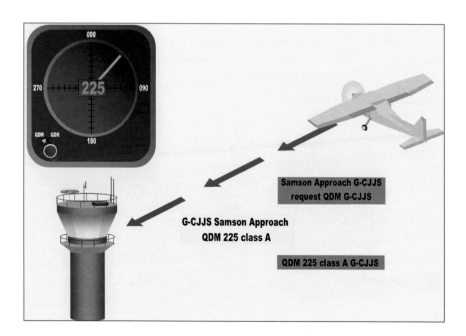

Samson Approach G-CJJS
request QDM G-CJJS

G-CJJS Samson Approach
QDM 225 class A

QDM 225 class A G-CJJS

QDR	Magnetic Bearing of the aircraft from the VDF station

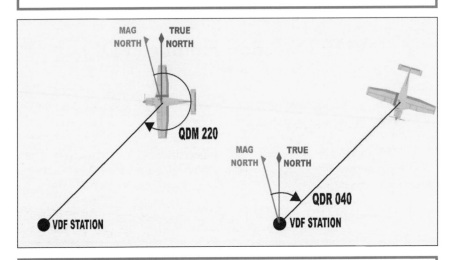

QTE	True bearing of the aircraft from the VDF station

QUJ	True bearing of the station from the aircraft

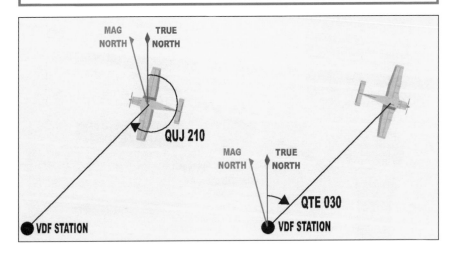

The phraseology is as follows:

Samson Homer **Golf- Charlie Juliet Juliet Sierra** request QDM Golf- Charlie Juliet Juliet Sierra

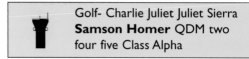

Golf- Charlie Juliet Juliet Sierra **Samson Homer** QDM two four five Class Alpha

QDM two four five Class Alpha **Golf- Charlie Juliet Juliet Sierra**

The callsign is repeated at the end of the request message so that the transmitted signal is of sufficient length for the ground equipment to establish the bearing.

VDF information is, again, a must readback item, as is the Class of bearing provided.

Class	Accuracy
A	+/-2°
B	+/- 5°
C	+/- 10°
D	Accuracy less than Class C

Flight Crossing Airways

A VFR aircraft needing to cross an airway should make the request to the appropriate ATS unit.

London Control **Golf-Oscar Hotel Echo Lima**

Golf-Oscar Hotel Echo Lima
London Control

Golf-Oscar Hotel Echo Lima, PA31 30 miles north of GOLES FL90, GOLES at 35 request clearance to cross airway B1 at GOLES

Golf-Oscar Hotel Echo Lima is cleared to cross B1 at GOLES FL90

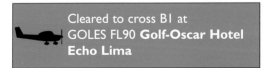
Cleared to cross B1 at GOLES FL90 **Golf-Oscar Hotel Echo Lima**

Golf-Echo Lima report GOLES

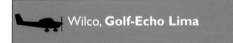
Wilco, **Golf-Echo Lima**

Chapter 3 - Part 8

In Flight Information

Danger Area Crossing Service/
Danger Area Activity Information Service

In-flight information on the status of selected Danger Areas is available from nominated units these are:

a. **Listed in the UK AIP**
b. **Detailed on the legend of the UK 1:500 000 chart**

The service provided will either be a Danger Area Crossing Service *(DACS pronounces "dacks")* or a Danger Area Activity Information Service *(DAAIS pronounced "day-iss")*. If no reply is obtained from the nominated unit, pilots are advised to assume that the relevant Danger Area is active.

Danger Area Crossing Service

When Danger Area activity permits the nominated service unit will provide a clearance to cross the area under a Radar Information Service or Flight Information Service.

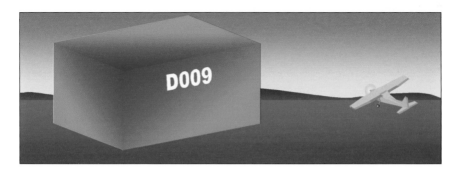

Plymouth Military **Golf- Charlie Juliet Juliet Sierra** request **Danger Area Crossing Service** of D009

 Golf- Charlie Juliet Juliet Sierra **Plymouth Military** Flight Information Service. D009 active. Report one zero miles from the boundary.

 Wilco, **Golf- Charlie Juliet Juliet Sierra**

 Golf- Charlie Juliet Juliet Sierra one zero miles from the boundary

 Golf- Juliet Sierra D009 remains active. Suggest re-route.

 Re-routing to the north **Golf- Juliet Sierra**

Or

 Golf- Charlie Juliet Juliet Sierra D009 not active, crossing approved report vacating the area.

 Crossing approved, Wilco **Golf- Charlie Juliet Juliet Sierra**

Golf- Charlie Juliet Juliet Sierra
vacating D009

Golf- Juliet Sierra roger, flight
information available from
London Information one two four
decimal seven five

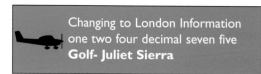
Changing to London Information
one two four decimal seven five
Golf- Juliet Sierra

Golf- Juliet Sierra roger

Danger Area Activity Information Service

The nominated unit will pass an update on the known status of the danger area. This information will assist the pilot in deciding whether it would be prudent to enter the Danger Area. This service does **not** constitute a clearance to cross a Danger Area. DAAIS is pronounced "DAY-ISS"

Lakenheath Radar **Golf- Charlie Juliet Juliet Sierra** request **day-iss for Thetford Range**

Golf- Charlie Juliet Juliet Sierra
Lakenheath Radar Thetford
active/not active

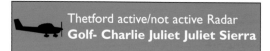
Thetford active/not active Radar
Golf- Charlie Juliet Juliet Sierra

VOLMET

VOLMET broadcasts include weather information for a group of airfields, as opposed to an ATIS broadcast which is particular to an individual airfield, the information contained is similar to that included in an ATIS broadcast. The specific frequencies are published in the UK AIP (**GEN**) and included in many flight guides.

The VOLMET content for each aerodrome includes:

- **Aerodrome name**
- **Time of origin**
- **Surface wind**
- **Visibility**
- **RVR, if applicable**
- **Weather**
- **Cloud**
- **Temperature and dew point**
- **QNH**
- **Trend**
- **Relevant items e.g. SNOCLO**

1. State the contents of a position report

2. What should you do if asked to "**squawk ident**" and "**squawk Charlie**"?

3. What is   **a.**   QDM ?
               b.   QDR ?

4. What is the accuracy of a **Class B VDF** bearing?

5. An ATSU states "**G-JS standby**", what should your response be?

6. **a.** To request a MATZ crossing the initial call should include what?
    b. At what range from the zone boundary should you make this call?
    c. Subsequently you are asked to "**pass your details**", which should be passed?

7. State the correct phraseology for obtaining a VDF bearing.

8. What special purpose transponder code means:

    a.   Emergency ?
    b.   Radio Failure ?
    c.   Hijack ?

9. At what range in terms of distance and time from a MATZ should you establish contact with the military controller?

10. What information is provided under RIS?

11. A LARS controller asks you to "**pass your message**", list the items you would pass.

Left Intentionally Blank

Chapter 4

Emergency Procedures

Left Intentionally Blank

Chapter 4 - Part 1

Introduction

There are two categories of emergency:

Distress

A condition of being threatened by grave and/or imminent danger and of requiring immediate assistance.

Spoken Word:　　　**MAYDAY**
Morse Code:　　　　**SOS** ••• --- •••

A distress message will take priority over all other messages

Urgency

A condition concerning the safety of an aircraft or other vehicle, or of some other person on board or within sight, but not requiring immediate assistance.

Spoken Word:　　　**PAN PAN**
Morse Code:　　　　**XXX** -••- -••- -••-

Emergency Frequencies

The first attempt to transmit an emergency message should be made on the frequency currently in use. If this is not possible the **Aeronautical Emergency Frequency 121.5MHz** should be used. An ATSU receiving the initial call may subsequently instruct the pilot to change to 121.5 if the controller decides that the Distress and Diversion Cell will be able to provide more appropriate assistance.

Emergency Facilities

The UK has two Distress and Diversion (**D&D**) cells, one at the London Area Control Centre *(callsign London Centre)* and one at the Scottish Area Control Centre *(callsign Scottish Centre)*, both are staffed by RAF personnel. Certain larger ATSUs and some Coastguard stations are also able to monitor 121.5MHz.

Chapter 4 - Part 2

Distress

It is most important to remember the order of priorities **AVIATE, NAVIGATE, COMMUNICATE**; in an emergency situation this is never more apposite, your main task is to continue to fly the aircraft safely. Nevertheless the more "natural" and efficient your call for help is, the more of your capacity is freed up to deal with the emergency situation. Additionally, the more required items you can pass to the controller, the less likely they are to interrupt you at an awkward moment, to obtain the missing information.

A distress call begins with the word **"MAYDAY"** spoken **three times**; the subsequent information should then be passed ideally in the order below *(obviously circumstances and time permitting!)*. MAYDAY is derived from the sound of the French phrase "m'aidez", meaning "Help Me!".

MAYDAY MAYDAY MAYDAY

N   –   Name of Station addressed
A   –   Aircraft Callsign
T   –   Type of Aircraft
N   –   Nature of Emergency
I   –   Intentions of Pilot-in-command
P   –   Present *(or last known)* Position; altitude/flight level; heading
P   –   Pilot Qualifications

         a.   Student Pilot or Tyro
         b.   No Instrument Qualification
         c.   IMC Rating
         d.   Full Instrument Rating

O   –   Other Useful Information,
         e.g. endurance, number on board

Although there is no ICAO requirement to include the pilot qualifications, in the UK it has been included as it is a useful indication to the controller as to the pilot's ability and whether flight in Instrument Meteorological Conditions would prove an additional hazard. When communicating with a military unit or the D&D cells, the word **"TYRO"** may be used to indicate a lack of experience, this will hopefully prevent them issuing complex instructions!

Should the call on the frequency in use not be acknowledged, transmit your intention to change to 121.5MHz and repeat the full **MAYDAY** call to "London or Scottish Centre".

Imposition of Silence

On hearing a distress call all other stations must maintain radio silence, but unless otherwise instructed should continue to monitor the frequency to ensure that assistance is being provided. Stations should take care not to interfere with the distress situation, but on hearing the call should WRITE DOWN as many details as possible in case there is a requirement to relay. Either the aircraft in distress or the station in control of a distress situation may impose radio silence, either en-masse or individually:

All stations **Cambridge Approach.** Stop transmitting, Mayday.

Or

Golf- Charlie Juliet Juliet Sierra **Cambridge Approach** stop transmitting, Mayday

Alternatively other aircraft may be transferred to a different frequency.

Mayday Golf- Bravo Uniform Golf Alpha. All other aircraft contact Luton Approach one two niner decimal five five.

Unacknowledged Distress Call

If the distress call is not acknowledged on the frequency currently in use the pilot should announce his/her intention to change to the International Emergency Frequency 121.5MHz. If an unacknowledged call is heard by you, the pilot, you should attempt to relay the message, but more on that to follow.

Cancellation of Distress

When an aircraft is no longer in distress the pilot should advise ATC as soon as practicable.

Example

Cranville Tower **Golf - Bravo Uniform Golf Alpha** cancel MAYDAY, engine restarted, request landing.

Golf-Golf Alpha runway one four, cleared to land surface wind one two zero, one zero

Runway one four cleared to land **Golf- Golf Alpha**

Had radio silence been imposed the following message will be transmitted, to indicate that normal working may resume:

All stations **Cambridge Approach** time one seven distress traffic Golf- Bravo Uniform Golf Alpha is ended.

SSR

An aircraft in distress should select the special purpose code 7700 as soon as practicable. However if the aircraft has already been assigned a discrete code by ATC this should be retained unless the controller instructs you to select 7700.

Emergency Scenario

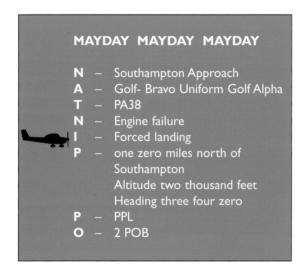

MAYDAY MAYDAY MAYDAY

N – Southampton Approach
A – Golf- Bravo Uniform Golf Alpha
T – PA38
N – Engine failure
I – Forced landing
P – one zero miles north of
        Southampton
        Altitude two thousand feet
        Heading three four zero
P – PPL
O – 2 POB

Golf- Bravo Uniform Golf Alpha
Southampton Approach,
roger MAYDAY.

All stations **Southampton Approach** stop transmitting.
MAYDAY

148

If original call is **not** acknowledged:

MAYDAY Golf- Bravo Uniform Golf Alpha changing to 121.5

MAYDAY MAYDAY MAYDAY

N	–	London Centre
A	–	Golf- Bravo Uniform Golf Alpha
T	–	PA38
N	–	Engine failure
I	–	Forced landing
P	–	one zero miles north of Southampton Altitude two thousand feet Heading three four zero
P	–	PPL
O	–	2 POB

Golf- Bravo Uniform Golf Alpha **London Centre** roger MAYDAY.

MAYDAY Golf- Bravo Uniform Golf Alpha CANCEL DISTRESS engine restarted diverting to Popham

Golf- Golf Alpha understand cancel distress.

Relayed **MAYDAY**

Should a distress call go unacknowledged by ATC then any station hearing the call must assume responsibility for ensuring that the message is passed. It could be that the aircraft in trouble is already too low for the signal to reach the ground station, remember that VHF is line of sight only. The most important thing is to make it clear that the aircraft transmitting is not itself in distress.

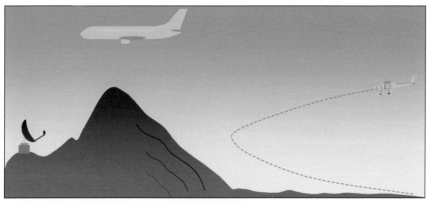

MAYDAY MAYDAY MAYDAY

N	–	Newcastle Approach Golf- Charlie Juliet Juliet Sierra has intercepted MAYDAY from Golf- Bravo Uniform Golf Alpha, I say again
A	–	Golf- Bravo Uniform Golf Alpha
T	–	PA38
N	–	Engine failure
I	–	Forced landing
P	–	two zero miles north west of Darlington Altitude eight hundred feet Heading three one zero
P	–	PPL
O	–	I POB

Golf- Charlie Juliet Juliet Sierra **Newcastle Approach** roger your relayed MAYDAY from Golf- Bravo Uniform Golf Alpha

You should continue to relay messages until the situation is resolved:

 All stations **Newcastle Approach** stop transmitting. MAYDAY.

 Golf- Charlie Juliet Juliet Sierra, cancel distress Golf- Bravo Uniform Golf Alpha has landed safely in a field, will telephone ATC Newcastle shortly.

 Golf-Juliet Sierra roger. All stations **Newcastle Approach** time one two zero one distress traffic Golf- Bravo Uniform Golf Alpha is ended.

Left Intentionally Blank

Chapter 4 - Part 3

Urgency

The main differences between **"urgency"** and **"distress"** are:

a. An urgency message is sent in a situation which requires increased attention, but which has **Not Yet** become a condition of **Grave & Imminent Danger.** *Note:* It is always possible to "up grade" should the situation deteriorate further
b. Urgency calls are second in priority to distress
c. There is no special purpose transponder code associated with urgency

The two conditions do share the same procedures for cancellation, and the need to relay.

An urgency message should be transmitted if the pilot experiences difficulties that compel him to land, but which do not require immediate assistance. The message could also concern another vehicle, or a person on board. E.g. another aircraft landed in a field, a seriously ill passenger, observing a life raft adrift. Anything that might endanger life if ignored.

The same mnemonic **NATNIPP** can be used for urgency calls:

PAN PAN, PAN PAN, PAN PAN

N – Luton Approach
A – Golf- Bravo Uniform
    Golf Alpha
T – PA38

N – Passenger with suspected
    heart attack
I – diverting to Luton request
    ambulance on arrival
P – overhead Henlow
    Altitude three thousand ft
    Heading two seven five
P – PPL/IR

Golf- Bravo Uniform Golf Alpha
Luton Approach, roger PAN.
QDM for Luton two one zero
Class Alpha. Enter the control
zone VFR not above altitude two
thousand ft Luton QNH niner
niner eight millibars.

QDM two one zero Class Alpha,
enter the zone VFR not above
altitude two thousand ft QNH
niner niner eight millibars **Golf-
Bravo Uniform Golf Alpha**

Golf- Golf Alpha the ambulance
service has been alerted. Report
field in sight.

Wilco, **Golf- Golf Alpha**

Chapter 4 - Part 4

Radio Failures

A total loss of radio communication equipment is an unlikely event. More usual would be a "**human error**" or a problem with either receiver or transmitter *(rarely do they both fail simultaneously)*.

As with most things it is best to examine the simple solutions first! On calling a unit and receiving no reply, before assuming the worst, check:

a. Have you selected the correct frequency *(not something similar but not exactly right!)?*

b. Are the headset jack plugs fully inserted? Is the headset itself or PTT button faulty? Try a hand mike or EPPT if available.

c. Is the volume set to an acceptable level? Ensure the squelch control is adjusted properly? **Note:** *Make sure during your training that your instructor shows you how to operate the squelch facility as this is often the cause of missed transmissions.*

d. Is the correct "**box**" selected?

e. If it is a pre-flight check could a hangar or other airfield feature be blocking your transmission? If airborne could you be too low? Remember VHF is line of sight only.

f. Is the station you are calling actually open? Try another frequency.

If the above have not found a solution it is time to delve a little deeper.

a. Can you hear "**sidetone**"? i.e. when you try to transmit can you hear yourself speaking?

b. Is the installation as a whole "**dead**"? Often the aircraft will be fitted with a combined NAV/COM, is the NAV part still serviceable?

c. CHECK
    i.   Battery/Master
    ii. Alternator and radio circuit breakers
    iii. Ammeter – does it show a discharge?

If the Receiver is Working

If you suspect transmitter failure, continue to listen out on the designated frequency. ATC may be able to use your carrier wave transmissions to communicate using the speechless code. Imaginative controllers may discern whether you can hear them by asking you to turn *(and seeing the "blip" that represents your aircraft turn)* or operate the transponder SPI feature.

The speechless code is a little like airborne "Twenty Questions", the controller will ask you questions to which you can only reply yes or no! Actually you do have a few more options, but in essence you key the PTT switch a certain number of times to reply as follows:

Speechless Code	
Number of Transmissions	**Meaning**
One short	YES or acknowledgement
Two short	NO
Three short	SAY AGAIN
Four short	REQUEST HOMING *(to the airfield)*, or used for initial alerting
One long (2 seconds)	MANOEUVRE COMPLETE *(e.g. steady on heading)*
One long, Two short, One long (letter X in Morse -••-)	MY AIRCRAFT HAS DEVELOPED ANOTHER EMERGENCY

You have attempted to establish communication, but have received no reply

Station calling **Cambridge Approach** is carrier wave only. Adopt the callsign "Speechless One". Are you inbound to Cambridge?

Press the transmit button once

Speechless One are you arriving from the North?

Press the transmit button twice

Speechless One are you inbound from the East?

Press the transmit button once

Speechless One roger expect straight in approach runway two three. Transmit four times when you have the airfield in sight.

Press the transmit button four times

Speechless One cleared to land runway two three surface wind two five zero one two knots.

VDF will still work on your carrier wave transmissions, in which case the controller will be able to provide you with a QDM to the airfield.

If the Transmitter is Working

Check to see if you can hear background noise *(using the squelch control)* or continuous broadcasts, such as ATIS or VOLMET. Change your headset; try the hand mike or EPPT. If all this is to no avail you can suspect receiver failure; as stated previously it is unusual for both the transmitter and receiver to fail simultaneously, so it is reasonable to assume the transmitter is still working. In this case you should "transmit blind", sending your message twice.

Duxford Information **Golf- Bravo Uniform Golf Alpha** transmitting blind one two two decimal zero seven due to receiver failure. Field in sight joining downwind left hand Runway two four. I say again Duxford Information **Golf- Bravo Uniform Golf Alpha** transmitting blind one two two decimal zero seven due to receiver failure. Field in sight joining downwind left hand Runway two four.

The **ATCO/FISO** will either advise other traffic to hold off or simply of your intentions.

Duxford Information **Golf- Bravo Uniform Golf Alpha** transmitting blind downwind Runway two four. I say again, Duxford Information **Golf- Bravo Uniform Golf Alpha** transmitting blind downwind Runway two four.

Duxford Information **Golf- Bravo Uniform Golf Alpha** transmitting blind final Runway two four. I say again, Duxford Information **Golf- Bravo Uniform Golf Alpha** transmitting blind final Runway two four.

Keep a Very Good Lookout !!

VFR

- Fly the Aircraft
- **Squawk 7600** and Mode **C**harlie
- Transmit Blind
- Stay in **VMC** and land at nearest suitable aerodrome. Remember the aircraft is not in immediate danger merely because the radio is not working.
- Notify the relevant **ATSU** on Landing

SVFR

- Fly the Aircraft
- **Squawk 7600** and Mode **C**harlie
- Transmit Blind
- If not in zone – **STAY OUT**
- If in Zone and inbound to the Aerodrome – Proceed in Accordance with Clearance
- In Zone Transiting – **LEAVE** by the most direct route
- Notify **ATC** as soon as possible after Landing

Left Intentionally Blank

Chapter 4 - Part 5

Distress & Diversion Cell

The UK has two Distress and Diversion Cells, one at each of the Area Control Centres (**ACC**). RAF personnel staff the sections with assistance being available from suitably equipped civil and military Air Traffic Control Units and certain HM Coastguard stations. They provide an emergency service on the International Aeronautical Emergency VHF frequency 121.5MHz for civil traffic and a similar service using UHF (**243MHz**) for military aircraft.

The service is available to all pilots flying within UK airspace who are in distress, in urgent need of assistance, or are experiencing difficulties which could lead to a state of emergency, such as uncertainty of position. If there is no real emergency in progress on either the VHF or UHF frequencies there is a provision for pilots to practise **urgency** procedures or training fixes.

The main function of the two D&D cells is to provide emergency aid and position fixing service for civil and military pilots. Over most of the London FIR to the south and east of Manchester an Autotriangulation (**DF**) service is available above 2000ft AMSL on 121.5MHz. For other areas DF bearings will have to be collated from several VDF stations, and therefore it will take a little longer to obtain a position fix, as once the bearings are obtained the aircraft position will be plotted on a 1:250000 aeronautical chart.

The accuracy of the position fix depends largely on the aircraft's altitude. The VHF fixing service is limited below 3000ft especially in areas of intervening high ground *(e.g. much of Wales, Scotland and SW England)*; detection of low flying aircraft may be severely limited. With no DF available, the controller will have to rely on the availability of other equipment, such as SSR, accuracy of pilot information regarding the route flown, last known position or reported landmarks to find the aircraft.

At certain UK aerodromes *(listed in the UKAIP)* emergency communication assistance is also available. Some maintain a listening watch on 121.5MHz, although may not necessarily be equipped with either VDF or SSR. Others, which do have VDF, may not have access to 121.5MHz, but may be able to provide a bearing to the D&D controller by landline. In such cases the pilot may be instructed to change frequency temporarily to that of the VDF station.

Practice Emergencies

Pilots may simulate urgency *(Pan)* incidents on 121.5MHz for training purposes and to experience the services available, but please note that the state of distress *(Mayday)* must **NOT** be practised. Before initiating the call you should listen out on the frequency to make sure that no actual emergency is being handled. The phraseology used emphasises the simulated nature of the exchange:

PRACTICE PAN, PRACTICE PAN, PRACTICE PAN London Centre **Golf- Bravo Uniform Golf Alpha**

The D&D controller will either accept the practice or advise you to call again at another time.

Golf- Bravo Uniform Golf Alpha **London Centre.** Continue with PRACTICE PAN.

If accepted, you should then pass the details of your flight.

Note: **DO NOT** select SSR code 7700 unless instructed to do so by the Emergency Controller.

Training Fix

Pilots may also use D & D to obtain a **'Training Fix'** on 121.5 MHz. These messages take precedence over practice emergency calls, but obviously not over actual emergencies. A training fix may be used to confirm your position if you do not want to make a practice pan call.

TRAINING FIX, TRAINING FIX, TRAINING FIX Golf- Hotel Alpha Charlie Kilo

Golf- Hotel Alpha Charlie Kilo your position is 15 miles north of Cranfield.

1. On what frequency should a "**MAYDAY**" call initially be transmitted?

2. Define   **a.**   Distress
          b.   Urgency

3. List the contents of a "**MAYDAY**"/"**PAN**" call.

4. Unless instructed to retain a discrete squawk, which code should be selected by aircraft in distress?

5. Who may impose radio silence?

6. What does the suffix "**TYRO**" indicate?

7. 121.5 may be used to practise emergency procedures, what condition must not be simulated?

8. You are flying in receipt of a RIS, twice you are asked to report your level and you have responded. The next call you hear is "**G-JS reply not received, if you read Bournemouth, turn left heading 040, I say again, turn left heading 040**". What has occurred?

Left Intentionally Blank

Chapter 5

"Test" Route in full Scenario

Aircraft: PA38 Tomahawk registration GCJJS
Departing: NORWICH
Destination: ELSTREE
Alternate: LUTON

FLIGHT PLAN.	Departure time: **1410**				
FROM	**TO**	**HDG**	**DIST**	**TIME**	**ALTITUDE**
Norwich	Wisbech	275	40nm	27	2000– FL40
Wisbech	Bassingbourn	200	35nm	23	FL40- 2000
Bassingbourn	Elstree	205	29nm	19	2000

Example Flight

Aircraft: PA38 Tomahawk registration GCJJS
Departing: NORWICH
Destination: ELSTREE
Alternate: LUTON

FLIGHT PLAN.	Departure time: 1410				
FROM	**TO**	**HDG**	**DIST**	**TIME**	**ALTITUDE**
Norwich	Wisbech	275	40nm	27	2000– FL40
Wisbech	Bassingbourn	200	35nm	23	FL40- 2000
Bassingbourn	Elstree	205	29nm	19	2000

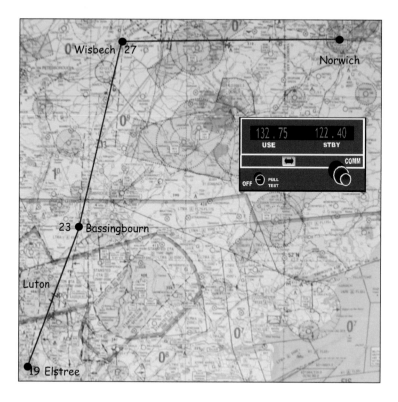

Departure

Begin by assuming you are in the aircraft with the engine running:

 Norwich Tower **Golf-Charlie Juliet Juliet** Sierra radio check one two four decimal two five.

 Golf-Charlie Juliet Juliet Sierra **Norwich Tower** readability five

 Readability five also, PA38 stand six request departure information **Golf-Charlie Juliet Juliet Sierra.**

 Golf-Juliet Sierra departure runway two seven, surface wind 240/08 knots, QNH 1007.

 Runway two seven, QNH 1007 **Golf-Juliet Sierra**

 Golf-Juliet Sierra request taxi

 Golf-Juliet Sierra taxi holding point A1 runway two seven, new QNH 1008

 Taxi holding point A1, runway two seven, QNH 1008 **Golf-Juliet Sierra**

 Golf-Juliet Sierra ready for departure

 Golf-Juliet Sierra after the landing Cherokee two mile final, line up runway two seven

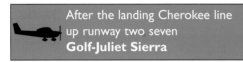 After the landing Cherokee line up runway two seven
Golf-Juliet Sierra

 Golf-Juliet Sierra runway two seven cleared for take off surface wind 250/10 knots.
Report reaching altitude two thousand feet.

 Cleared for take off, Wilco
Golf-Juliet Sierra

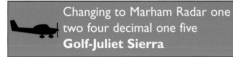 **Golf-Juliet Sierra** level altitude two thousand feet

 Golf-Juliet Sierra roger freecall en-route frequency

Changing to Marham Radar one two four decimal one five
Golf-Juliet Sierra

 Marham Radar **Golf-Charlie Juliet Juliet Sierra** request MATZ penetration

 Golf-Charlie Juliet Juliet Sierra **Marham Radar** pass your details

 **Golf-Charlie Juliet Juliet Sierra**
PA38
P 5 miles east of Shipdham
H heading two seven zero
A altitude two thousand ft, QNH 1008
C VFR
E estimating MATZ boundary at 26

 Golf-Juliet Sierra set Marham QFE 1001

Marham QFE 1001 set **Golf- Juliet Sierra**

 Golf-Juliet Sierra cross MATZ at two thousand feet on Marham QFE 1001, report entering and leaving the MATZ

 Cross MATZ at two thousand feet Marham QFE 1001, Wilco **Golf- Juliet Sierra**

 Golf- Juliet Sierra entering MATZ

 Golf-Juliet Sierra roger

 **Golf-Juliet Sierra** leaving MATZ request Radar Information Service

 Golf-Juliet Sierra roger squawk three six six seven

 Squawk 3667 **Golf-Juliet Sierra**

 Golf-Juliet Sierra identified eight miles west of Marham, Radar Information Service

 Radar Information Service **Golf-Juliet Sierra**

 Golf-Juliet Sierra unknown traffic two o'clock five miles crossing right to left indicating three thousand feet unverified.

Note: **Unverified** - meaning the controller has not checked the accuracy
of the Mode C readout against a report from the pilot,
but is using the information to give you an idea where to look.

 Visual **Golf-Juliet Sierra**

 Golf-Juliet Sierra squawk Charlie

 Unable to comply negative mode Charlie **Golf-Juliet Sierra**

A Golf-Charlie Juliet Juliet Sierra
P turning at Wisbech
T time 37
L climbing flight level four zero
N estimating Bassingbourn
E time 1500

Golf-Juliet Sierra report reaching flight level four zero

 Golf-Juliet Sierra maintaining flight level four zero

 Golf-Juliet Sierra roger.

You then overhear the following call which remains unacknowledged by the Marham Radar controller. What action should you take?

MAYDAY, MAYDAY, MAYDAY. Marham Radar GBUGA Tomahawk, engine failure, forced landing five miles east of March one thousand feet heading 170 PPL

MAYDAY, MAYDAY, MAYDAY
N Marham Radar
A **GCJJS** have intercepted Mayday from GBUGA, I say again GBUGA
T Tomahawk
N Engine failure
I Forced landing
P 5 miles east of March, one thousand feet, heading 170
P PPL
O 1 POB

 Mayday Golf-Juliet Sierra roger your relayed mayday from GBUGA. Break all stations **Marham Radar**, stop transmitting, Mayday.

MAYDAY Golf-Juliet Sierra this is G-GA cancel distress, landed safely will telephone Marham ATC

 MAYDAY G-JS Cancel Distress G-GA has landed safely and will telephone Marham ATC

 G-JS roger. Mayday all stations, **Marham Radar** time 29 distress traffic GBUGA is ended

 G-JS approaching the edge of my radar cover, squawk seven thousand, radar service terminated. Position is 30 miles south west of Marham.

 Squawk seven thousand, radar service terminated. Request frequency change to Cambridge Approach 123.6. **G-JS**

 G-JS frequency change approved.

Obtain a VDF bearing from Cambridge

 Cambridge Approach **GCJJS** request QDM GCJJS

 GCJJS **Cambridge Approach** QDM 330 Class Alpha

 QDM 330 Class Alpha **GCJJS**

 GCJJS changing to Luton Radar 129.55

 G-JS roger

Luton Approach **GCJJS**

 GCJJS **Luton Approach** pass your message

**GCJJS PA38** Norwich to Elstree
P overhead Bassingbourn
H heading 200
A altitude two thousand feet,
  QNH 1000
C VFR
R request zone transit on track
  Elstree

 G-JS flight information service Luton QNH niner niner niner millibars.

 QNH niner niner niner millibars **G-JS**

 G-JS squawk 4662

 Squawk 4662 **G-JS**

 GCJJS identified two miles south west of Bassingbourn transit the Luton Control Zone VFR on track Elstree not above altitude two thousand feet

 Transit the control zone VFR on track Elstree not above altitude two thousand feet **GCJJS**

Your engine begins to run roughly, however you are not in immediate danger.
What message will you transmit?

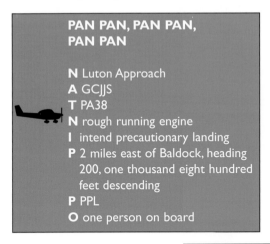

**PAN PAN, PAN PAN,
PAN PAN**

N Luton Approach
A GCJJS
T PA38
N rough running engine
I intend precautionary landing
P 2 miles east of Baldock, heading
   200, one thousand eight hundred
   feet descending
P PPL
O one person on board

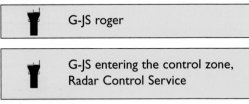

G-JS roger pan

Engine power is now restored and you intend to continue to Elstree:

G-CJJS cancel urgency engine
power restored continuing to
Elstree

G-JS roger

G-JS entering the control zone,
Radar Control Service

Radar Control Service **G-JS**

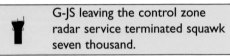

G-JS leaving the control zone
radar service terminated squawk
seven thousand.

Radar service terminated, squawk seven thousand **G-JS**

 G-JS freecall Elstree Information one two two decimal four

 Freecall Elstree Information one two two decimal four **G-JS**

Arrival

 Elstree Information **GCJJS**

 GCJJS **Elstree Information** pass your message

GCJJS PA38

P overhead Hatfield disused
H heading two zero zero
A altitude two thousand feet, QNH 999 millibars
C VFR
E estimating Elstree at 19
R request joining instructions

 G-JS runway two six, QFE niner niner seven millibars report downwind left hand, two aircraft in the circuit

Runway two six, QFE niner niner seven millibars join downwind left hand **G-JS**

 G-JS downwind

 G-JS roger report final, a Seneca one mile final

 Wilco, **G-JS**

 G-JS final

 G-JS Elstree runway blocked - aircraft with collapsed undercarriage, estimated time to reopening niner zero minutes. Request your intentions.

 G-JS Going Around

 **G-JS** Diverting to Luton

 G-JS roger, report leaving the frequency.

 Changing to Luton Radar one two niner decimal five five **G-JS**

Luton Radar **GCJJS**

 GCJJS **Luton Radar** pass your message

 GCJJS PA38 Inbound
P north of Elstree
H heading 340
A climbing to altitude two
   thousand feet, QNH 997 millibars
C VFR
E estimating Luton at two five
R request zone entry and joining
   instructions

 G-JS squawk 4667

 Squawk 4667 **G-JS**

 G-JS identified one one miles south of Luton. Enter the control zone VFR not above altitude two thousand feet, route direct to Luton, report field in sight.

 Enter the control zone VFR not above altitude two thousand feet, route direct to Luton, Wilco **G-JS**

G-JS Information Tango, Luton QNH niner niner niner millibars, runway in use two six.

 Information Tango, Luton QNH niner niner niner millibars, runway two six **G-JS.**

 G-JS field in sight

 G-JS join left base runway two six

 Join left base runway two six, **G-JS**

 G-JS contact Luton Tower one three two decimal five five.

 Contact Luton Tower one three two decimal five five, **G-JS.**

 Luton Tower **GCJJS**

 GCJJS report left base runway two six QFE niner eight eight millibars

 QFE niner eight eight millibars, Wilco **G-JS**

 **G-JS** left base runway two six

 G-JS orbit right, traffic is a Boeing 737 5 mile final, report when you have that traffic in sight.

 Orbit right **G-JS**

Visual with the Boeing 737 **G-JS**

 G-JS report final number two runway two six, follow the Boeing 737 caution vortex wake recommended spacing six miles.

 Report final number two **G-JS**

 G-JS final

 G-JS runway two six cleared to land, surface wind three two zero, eight knots

 Runway two six cleared to land **G-JS**

 G-JS taxi holding point Bravo Two, contact Luton Ground one two one decimal seven five.

 Taxi holding point Bravo Two, contact Luton Ground one two one decimal seven five **G-JS**

 Luton Ground **GCJJS**

 GCJJS Luton Ground hold Bravo Two, after the outbound Boeing 757 left to right follow the marshaller to stand 51

 After the Boeing 757 follow the marshaller to stand 51 **G-JS**

Left Intentionally Blank

Chapter 6

IMC Procedures

Introduction

The preceding chapters will hopefully have helped you to negotiate the initial PPL examinations successfully and to obtain a reasonable level of competence and confidence. Congratulations! The following chapter is intended to give you examples of the radiotelephony procedures required should you decide to continue your training towards an IMC rating.

Chapter 6 - Part 1

Departures

Introduction

Instrument departures will receive a clearance to depart the aerodrome either:

i.   Following a Standard Instrument Departure (SID)
ii.   Following a Standard Departure Route (SDR), or
iii. Following specific instructions from the appropriate ATC unit

Standard Instrument Departures

A SID is a procedure where the levels and tracks to be flown by aircraft have been predetermined and published.

This enables RT workload to be greatly reduced. The controller will pass the appropriate SID designator and number, rather than transmitting more complicated routing and level instructions. Also included on the SID chart will be the frequency to expect after departure, rates of climb to achieve, RT failure instructions and any other local instructions. SIDs are usually designed for traffic wishing to join airways.

The SID name is composed of the:

i.   Name of the last beacon on the route
ii.   The version of the SID (each time there is an amendment the number will increase), and
iii. A letter signifying the departure runway

Example

London City Airport has two SIDs terminating at the Brookmans Park beacon, the BPK 5U leaves from runway 10 and the BPK 5T leaves from runway 28.

G-JS your clearance

 G-JS pass your message

 GCJJS cleared to Amsterdam Clacton 5 Charlie departure, squawk 3442

 Cleared to Amsterdam Clacton 5 Charlie departure, squawk 3442 **GCJJS**

 G-JS readback correct

 G-AH your clearance

 G-AH pass your message

 GHBAH cleared to Edinburgh Brookmans Park 5 Tango departure, squawk 6566

 Cleared to Edinburgh Brookmans Park 5 Tango departure, squawk 6566 **GHBAH**

 G-AH readback correct

Standard Departure Routes

SDRs are similar to SIDs in that the levels and tracks to be flown have been predetermined and published, however they are intended to be used by aircraft leaving controlled airspace.

G-MO your clearance

 G-MO pass your message

 GMOMO cleared to leave the control zone IFR standard departure route X-ray, squawk 5435

 Cleared to leave the control zone IFR standard departure route X-ray, squawk 5435 **GMOMO**

ATC Instructions

If the standard routes are not appropriate or have not been prepared at a particular aerodrome the aircraft will be given specific instructions to follow. These instructions will include the track, level squawk and frequency to expect after departure.

G-CK your clearance

 **G-CK** pass your message

 GHACK leave the control zone IFR radar heading 060, climb to altitude four thousand feet, squawk 7023 frequency 129.82 when instructed.

 Leave the control zone IFR radar heading 060, climb to altitude four thousand feet, squawk 7023 frequency 129.82 when instructed **GHACK**.

Hopefully you can see merely from the examples *(page 181)* how the use of SIDs and SDRs reduce the radio workload.

Chapter 6 - Part 2

Instrument Arrivals

Introduction

Approach Control will normally advise the aircraft of the type of approach to be expected.

ILS AND OTHER PILOT-INTERPRETED APPROACHES
Example ATC phraseologies:

Vectoring for approach:

- Vectoring for (type of pilot-interpreted aid) approach runway (number)
- Vectoring for visual approach runway (number) report field (or runway) in sight
- Vectoring for surveillance radar approach runway (number)
- Vectoring for a precision approach runway (number)

Example ATC phraseologies

Vectoring for ILS and other pilot-interpreted aids:

- Position (number) miles (or kilometres) from (fix). Turn left (or right) heading (three digits)
- Closing from left (or right) report established
- Report established on ILS localizer
- Turn left (or right) heading (three digits) to intercept [or report established]
- This turn will take you through (aid) (reason)
- Maintain (altitude) until glidepath interception

Bournemouth Approach **GBREN**
FL60 estimating SAM 46
information Delta

 GBREN Bournemouth Approach
descend to altitude 4000 feet,
QNH 1022 expect ILS approach
runway 26

 Descend to altitude 4000 feet, ILS
runway 26, QNH 1022, **GBREN**

EXAMPLE ILS PHRASEOLOGY

 GFKCS expect ILS approach
runway 23, QNH 1014

 Runway 23, QNH 1014, request
straight in approach on ILS
GFKCS

 G-CS cleared straight in
approach, report established

 Cleared straight in approach,
wilco **G-CS**

 G-CS established

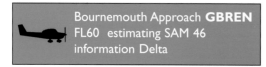 G-CS descend with the ILS
contact Coventry Tower 118.7

 Descend with the ILS contact
Coventry Tower 118.7 **G-CS**

 Coventry Tower **GFKCS**

 GFKCS Coventry Tower report outer marker

 Wilco **GFKCS**

 **GFKCS** outer marker

 G-CS runway 23 cleared to land, wind 280 15

 Cleared to land **G-CS**

For greater accuracy marker beacons are gradually being replaced with Distance Measuring Equipment with the range electronically set to the appropriate runway threshold. Likewise the phrase "report outer marker" is gradually being replaced with a request to report at a specific DME range. E.g. "GAVXF report 6 DME"

EXAMPLE RADAR VECTORED ILS PHRASEOLOGY

The example below is a training approach. Missed approach instructions will be passed to the pilot at an early stage in the approach, or you will be advised to expect the "standard missed approach".

 East Midlands Approach **GBTNT** descending to altitude four thousand feet, information Delta

GBTNT East Midlands Approach vectoring for an ILS approach runway 27, information Delta QNH 999 millibars.

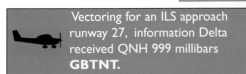 Vectoring for an ILS approach runway 27, information Delta received QNH 999 millibars **GBTNT.**

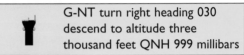 G-NT turn right heading 030 descend to altitude three thousand feet QNH 999 millibars

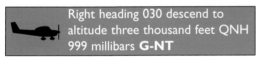 Right heading 030 descend to altitude three thousand feet QNH 999 millibars **G-NT**

G-NT descend to altitude two thousand feet, turn right heading 280, downwind left hand 20 miles from touchdown

 Descend to altitude two thousand feet turn right heading 280 **G-NT**

 G-NT after missed approach climb straight ahead to altitude two thousand feet, on reaching turn left to leave the control zone on track IFR

 After missed approach climb straight ahead to altitude two thousand feet, on reaching turn left to leave the control zone on track IFR **G-NT**

 G-NT turn left heading 350 base leg

 Left heading 350 **G-NT**

 G-NT turn left heading 300, closing the localiser from the left report established, eight miles from touchdown

 Left heading 300, report established **G-NT**

 Localiser established **G-NT**

 G-NT descend with the glidepath, threshold elevation 306 feet

 Descend with the glidepath **G-NT**

 G-NT runway 27 cleared low approach and go around not below height 400ft above threshold elevation inspection vehicle on the runway, report going around

 Runway 27 cleared low approach and go around not below height 400ft above threshold elevation, Wilco **G-NT**

 G-NT going around

 G-NT roger

Surveillance Radar Approach (SRA)

An SRA is a non-precision approach during which the air traffic controller will pass vectors to position the aircraft on final approach for a runway, the intention being that once the approach is completed a visual landing will be made. Advisory heights or altitudes are passed either at one mile or half mile intervals depending on the range at which the approach will terminate.

Golf-Hotel Bravo Alpha Hotel this will be a surveillance radar approach, runway 18, terminating at 2 miles from touchdown. 3-degree glidepath. Check your minima; step down fixes and missed approach point.

 Golf-Hotel Bravo Alpha Hotel

Golf – Alpha Hotel report runway or approach lights in sight.
After landing contact
Ewing Tower 118.25

After landing Ewing Tower 118.25,
Wilco **Golf- Alpha Hotel**

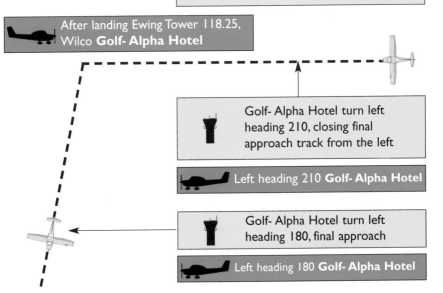

Golf- Alpha Hotel turn left heading 210, closing final approach track from the left

Left heading 210 **Golf- Alpha Hotel**

Golf- Alpha Hotel turn left heading 180, final approach

Left heading 180 **Golf- Alpha Hotel**

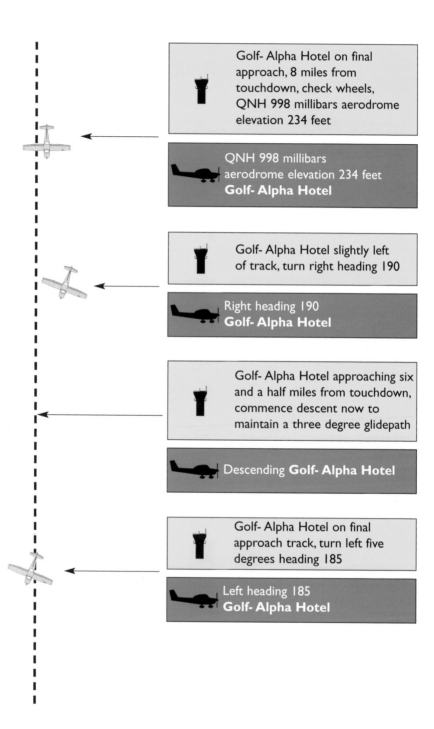

Golf- Alpha Hotel on final approach, 8 miles from touchdown, check wheels, QNH 998 millibars aerodrome elevation 234 feet

QNH 998 millibars aerodrome elevation 234 feet **Golf- Alpha Hotel**

Golf- Alpha Hotel slightly left of track, turn right heading 190

Right heading 190 **Golf- Alpha Hotel**

Golf- Alpha Hotel approaching six and a half miles from touchdown, commence descent now to maintain a three degree glidepath

Descending **Golf- Alpha Hotel**

Golf- Alpha Hotel on final approach track, turn left five degrees heading 185

Left heading 185 **Golf- Alpha Hotel**

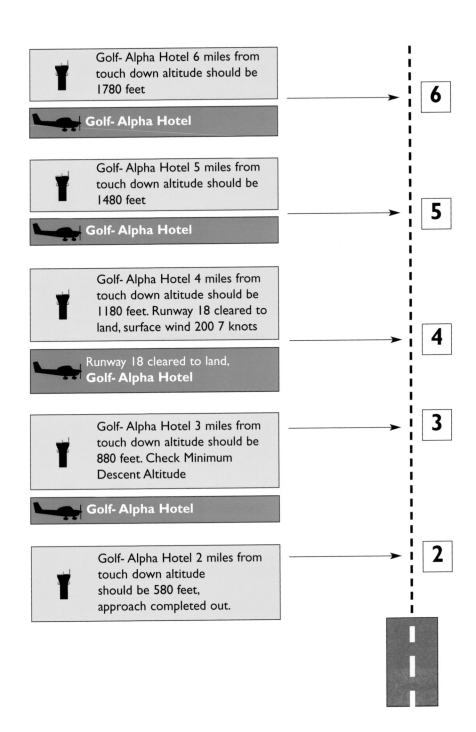

NDB Approaches

 GLYNY request rejoin, information Charlie estimating CIT at 48

 GLYNY cleared to the CIT at altitude four thousand five hundred feet squawk 7017 Charlie current Runway 22 QNH 1001

 Cleared to the CIT at altitude four thousand five hundred feet QNH 1001 squawk 7017 runway 22 **GLYNY**

 G-NY report reaching four thousand five hundred feet and entering the hold CIT

 Wilco **G-NY**

 G-NY four thousand five hundred feet

 G-NY roger

 G-NY CIT entering the hold

 G-NY report ready for the approach

 Wilco **G-NY**

 G-NY ready for approach

 G-NY descend to altitude three thousand five hundred feet report reaching.

 Descend to altitude three thousand five hundred feet, wilco **G-NY**

G-NY three thousand five hundred feet

 G-NY report beacon outbound

 Report beacon outbound **G-NY**

 G-NY beacon outbound

 G-NY cleared NDB approach runway 22 report base turn complete

 Cleared NDB approach runway 22 report base turn complete **G-NY**

 G-NY base turn complete

 G-NY report beacon inbound

 Wilco **G-NY**

 G-NY beacon inbound

 G-NY threshold elevation 358 feet contact Cranfield Tower 134.92

 Contact Cranfield Tower 134.92 **G-NY**

Holding Procedures

Normally holding procedures should be published. If a pilot requires a detailed description of the holding procedure based on a facility, the following phraseology will be used.

To assist the pilot controllers should pass the information in the following format.

- **Fix**
- **Level**
- **Inbound track**
- **Right or left turns**
- **Time of leg**

 Bonus 89 hold at CT FL60

 Request holding instructions Bonus 89

 Bonus 89 hold at CT NDB FL60, inbound track 230 degrees left hand pattern, outbound time 1 minute

Aide-Memoire

Inbound Call

Callsign
Type

P – point of departure
& present position
H – heading
A – altitude/FL
C – conditions VFR/IFR
E – ETA or en-route to/from
R – "Request joining instructions"

MATZ Penetration

Station
Callsign
"Request MATZ penetration"
(pass your message)
Callsign
P – position
H – heading
A – altitude/FL
C – conditions VFR/IFR
E – estimate for MATZ

SVFR Details

C – callsign
T – type
I – intentions
E – ETA for zone boundary

VDF

Station Callsign
Aircraft Callsign
Request QDM
Aircraft Callsign

LARS

Station
Callsign
"Request Lower Airspace
Radar Service" *(pass your message)*
Callsign
Type
Departure & destination
P – position
H – heading
A – altitude/FL
F – flight rules
T – type of service requested

Distress

MAYDAY MAYDAY MAYDAY

N – name of station called
A – aircraft callsign
T – type of aircraft
N – nature of emergency
I – intentions
P – position, level, heading
P – pilot qualifications
O – other useful information

Position Report

A – Aircraft callsign
P – position
T – time
L – level
N – next reporting point
E – ETA for next reporting point

Urgency

PAN PAN, PAN PAN, PAN PAN
N – name of station called
A – aircraft callsign
T – type of aircraft
N – nature of emergency
I – intentions
P – position, level, heading
P – pilot qualifications
O – other useful information

1. Roger means: I have received your last transmission.
Wilco means: I understand your message and will comply with it.

2. **a.** MONARCH NY
b. G-XY

3. **"Aeronautical Station"**: A land station in the aeronautical mobile service. In certain instances, an aeronautical station may be placed on board a ship or an earth satellite.

4. **a.** Five five or one three five five; one five zero zero
b. Altitude two thousand four hundred feet
c. One two six decimal seven two

5. Taxi instructions
Level instructions
Heading instructions
Speed instructions
Airways or route clearances
Runway in use
Clearance to enter, land on, take off on, backtrack or hold short
of an active runway
SSR operating instructions
Altimeter settings
VDF information
Frequency changes
Type of radar service

6. Distress
    Urgency
    Communications relating to direction finding
    Flight safety messages
    Meteorological messages
    Flight regularity messages

7. Air Traffic Control
    Flight Information
    Air/ground

8. Duxford Information.

9. Bourn Radio.

10. Only after the ground station has abbreviated the callsign first.

11. Affirm or Negative.

12. Immediately before the word height or altitude.

13. Callsign
    The condition
    Identification of the subject of the condition
    The instruction

14. Unable comply.

15. i.   QFE - height
    ii. QNH - altitude
    iii. 1013mb – flight level

16. On initial contact with an ATSU, when reading back an ATC route clearance, or when specifically instructed by an ATSU.

Answers   Chapter 2

1. Readable but with difficulty, perfectly readable.

2. "*(Callsign)* **ready for departure**".

3. Automatic Terminal Information Service.

4. Only to acknowledge an ATC clearance to take off *(or cancellation thereof)*.

5. Callsign, type, intentions and ETA for the zone boundary.

6. Initiate a missed approach. "**Going around** *(callsign)*".

7. SVFR means a flight made at any time in a Class A control zone or in any
    other control zone in IMC or at night in respect of which ATC has given
    permission for the flight to be made in accordance with special instructions
    given by that unit instead of in accordance with the Instrument Flight Rules.

8. Between 8 and 4 miles.

9. Information useful for the safe and efficient conduct of flights in the ATZ.

10. Either simply acknowledge with your callsign or transmit your intentions
    "**G-CS**" or "**Landing G-CS**".

11. Transmit nothing and wait to be called.

Left Intentionally Blank

1. Aircraft callsign
    Position
    Time
    Level
    Next reporting point
    ETA for that reporting point

2. "**Squawk ident**" means operate the SPI feature and "**squawk Charlie**" means select altitude reporting.

3. a.   QDM Magnetic heading to be steered by the aircraft *(assuming nil wind)* to reach the station.
    b.   QDR Magnetic bearing of the aircraft from the station

4. +/- 5°

5. Nothing, remain silent and wait to be called.

6. a.   The initial call should include the phrase "**Request MATZ penetration**".
    b.   This call should be made 15nm or 5 minutes flying time from the boundary whichever is sooner.
    c.   Subsequent information:

    P   –   position
    H   –   heading
    A   –   altitude/FL
    C   –   conditions VFR/IFR
    E   –   estimate for MATZ

7. *(Station being called) (Full callsign)* request QDM *(Full callsign)*.

8. a.   **Emergency**   **7700**
    b.   **Radio failure**   **7600**
    c.   **Hijack**   **7500**

9. 15nm or 5 minutes flying time from the boundary whichever is sooner.

10. Traffic information including bearing, distance and if known level of conflicting aircraft.

11. Callsign - Type - Departure & destination

P – **Position**
H – **Heading**
A – **Altitude/FL**
F – **Flight rules**
T – **Type of service requested**

1. The frequency currently in use.

2. **a.** Distress: A condition of being threatened by grave and/or imminent danger and of requiring immediate assistance.

   b. Urgency: A condition concerning the safety of an aircraft or other vehicle, or of some other person on board or within sight, but not requiring immediate assistance.

3. **MAYDAY MAYDAY MAYDAY/PAN PAN,PAN PAN,PAN PAN**

N	–	name of station addressed.
A	–	aircraft callsign.
T	–	type of aircraft.
N	–	nature of emergency.
I	–	intentions of pilot-in-command
P	–	present (or last known) position; altitude/flight level; heading.
P	–	pilot qualifications

   e. Student pilot or Tyro
   f. No instrument qualification
   g. IMC rating
   h. Full instrument rating

O	–	other useful information, e.g. endurance, number on board.

4. 7700.

5. An Air Traffic Control Unit.

6. A low time or limited experience pilot.

7. Distress must not be simulated.

8. Your transmitter has probably failed.

Left Intentionally Blank

Aerodrome Control Services

Air traffic control service for aerodrome traffic.

Aerodrome Flight Information Service

A flight information service provided to aerodrome traffic.

Aerodrome Traffic

All traffic on the manoeuvring area of an aerodrome and all traffic flying in the vicinity of an aerodrome.

Note: An aircraft is in the vicinity of an aerodrome when it is in, entering or leaving an aerodrome traffic circuit.

Aerodrome Traffic Circuit

The specified path to be flown by aircraft operating in the vicinity of an aerodrome

Aeronautical Mobile Service

A mobile service between aeronautical stations and aircraft stations, or between aircraft stations, in which survival craft stations may participate; emergency position-indicating radio beacon stations may also participate in this service on designated distress and emergency frequencies.

Aeronautical Station

A land station in the aeronautical mobile service. In certain instances, an aeronautical station may be located, for example, on board ship or on a platform at sea.

Air-Ground Communication Service

A service that permits information to be passed from an aeronautical station to an aircraft on or in the vicinity of an aerodrome.

Air Traffic

All aircraft in flight or operating on the manoeuvring area of an aerodrome.

Air Traffic Control Clearance

Authorisation for an aircraft to proceed under conditions specified by an air traffic control unit

Air Traffic Service

A generic term meaning variously, flight information service, alerting service, air traffic advisory service, air traffic control service, area control service, approach control service or aerodrome control service.

Air Traffic Services Unit

A generic term meaning variously, air traffic control unit, flight information centre or air traffic services reporting office.

Airway

A control area or portion thereof established in the form of a corridor equipped with radio navigation aids.

Altitude   The vertical distance of a level, a point or an object considered as a point measured from mean sea level (MSL)

Approach Control Service

ATC service for arriving or departing controlled flights.

Apron

A defined area, on a land aerodrome, intended to accommodate aircraft for the purposes of loading or unloading passengers, mail or cargo, fuelling, parking or maintenance.

Area Control Centre

A unit established to provide Air Traffic Control Service to controlled flights in control areas under its jurisdiction.

Automatic Terminal Information Service

The provision of current, routine information to arriving and departing aircraft by means of a continuous and repetitive broadcast throughout the day or a specified portion of the day.

Blind Transmission

A transmission from one station to another station in circumstances where two-way communication cannot be established but where it is believed the called station is able to receive the transmission.

Broadcast
A transmission of information relating to air navigation that is not addressed to a specific station or stations.

Clearance Limit
The point to which an aircraft is granted an Air Traffic Control Clearance.

Controlled Airspace
An airspace of defined dimensions within which Air Traffic Control Service is provided to IFR flights and to VFR flights in accordance with the airspace classification.

Control Zone
A controlled airspace extending upwards from the surface of the earth to a specified upper limit.

Expected Approach Time
The time at which ATC expects that an arriving aircraft, following a delay, will leave the holding point to complete its approach for a landing.

Flight Information Centre
A unit established to provide flight information service and alerting service.

Flight Information Service
A service provided for the purpose of giving advice and information useful for the safe and efficient conduct of flights.

Flight Plan
Specified information provided to Air Traffic Services Units, relative to an intended flight or portion of a flight of an aircraft.

Heading
The direction in which the longitudinal axis of an aircraft is pointed, usually expressed in degrees from North (true, magnetic, compass or grid).

Holding Point
A specified location, identified by visual or other means, in the vicinity of which the position of an aircraft in flight is maintained in accordance with ATC clearances.

Holding Procedure

A pre-determined manoeuvre which keeps an aircraft within a specified airspace while awaiting further clearance.

IFR Flight

A flight conducted in accordance with instrument flight rules.

Instrument Meteorological Conditions

Meteorological conditions expressed in terms of visibility, distance from cloud, and ceiling, less than the minima specified for visual meteorological conditions.

Level

A generic term relating to the vertical position of an aircraft in flight and meaning variously, height, altitude or flight level.

Manoeuvring Area
That part of an aerodrome to be used for the take-off, landing and taxiing of aircraft, excluding aprons.

Missed Approach Procedure

The procedure to be followed if the approach cannot be continued.

Movement Area

That part of an aerodrome to be used for the take-off, landing and taxiing of aircraft, consisting of the manoeuvring area and the aprons.

Radar Approach

An approach in which the final approach phase is executed under the direction of a radar controller.

Radar Identification

The situation which exists when the radar position of a particular aircraft is seen on a radar display and positively identified by the ATC controller.

Radar Vectoring

Provision of navigational guidance to aircraft in the form of specific headings, based on the use of radar.

Reporting Point

A specified geographical location in relation to which the position of an aircraft can be reported.

Runway Visual Range (RVR)

The range over which the pilot of an aircraft on the centre line of a runway can see the runway surface markings or the lights delineating the runway or identifying its centre line

Touchdown

The point where the nominal glide path intercepts the runway.

Track

The projection on the earth's surface of the path of an aircraft, the direction of which path at any point is usually expressed in degrees from North (true, magnetic or grid).

VFR Flight

A flight conducted in accordance with the visual flight rules.

Visual Approach

An approach by an IFR flight when either part or all of an instrument approach procedure is not completed and the approach is executed with visual reference to terrain.

Visual Meteorological Conditions

Meteorological conditions expressed in terms of visibility, distance from cloud, and ceiling equal to or better than the specified minima.

Left Intentionally Blank

Common Abbreviations

The abbreviations listed below are normally spoken using the constituent letters, rather than the spelling alphabet, except that those indicated by an asterisk are normally spoken as complete words.

Abbreviation	Meaning
ACAS*	Airborne Collision Avoidance System
ACC	Area control centre or area control
ADF	Automatic direction finding equipment
ADR	Advisory route
AFIS	Aerodrome flight information service
AGL	Above ground level
AIP	Aeronautical information publication
AIRAC*	Aeronautical information regulation and control
AIS	Aeronautical information service
AMSL	Above mean sea level
ATC	Air traffic control (in general)
ATD	Actual time of departure
ATFM	Air traffic flow management
ATIS*	Automatic terminal information service
ATS	Air traffic service
ATZ	Air traffic zone
CAVOK*	Visibility. cloud and present weather better than prescribed values or conditions
CTR	Control zone
DME	Distance measuring equipment
EET	Estimated elapsed time
ETA	Estimated time of arrival or estimating arrival
ETD	Estimated time of departure or estimating departure
FIC	Flight information centre
FIR	Flight information region
FIS	Flight information service
GCA	Ground controlled approach system or ground controlled approach
HF	High frequency (3 - 30 MHz)
H24	Continuous day and night service
IFR	Instrument flight rules
ILS	Instrument landing system
IMC	Instrument meteorological conditions
INFO*	Information
INS	Inertial navigation system
LORAN*	Long range navigation system
MET*	Meteorological or meteorology
MLS	Microwave landing system
MNPS	Minimum navigation performance specifications
NDB	Non-directional beacon
NIL*	None or I have nothing to send you
NOTAM*	A notice distributed by means of telecommunication containing information concerning the establishment. condition or change in any aeronautical facility, service, procedure or hazard, the timely knowledge of which is essential to personnel concerned with flight operations
QFE	Atmospheric pressure at aerodrome elevation (or at runway threshold)
QNH	Altimeter sub-scale setting to obtain elevation when on the ground
RCC	Rescue co-ordination centre

Abbreviation	Meaning
RNAV*	Area navigation
RVR	Runway visual range
SELCAL*	A system which permits the selective calling of individual aircraft over radiotelephone channels linking a ground station with the aircraft
SID*	Standard instrument departure
SIGMET*	Information concerning en-route weather phenomena which may affect the safety of aircraft operations
SNOWTAM*	A special series of NOTAM notifying the presence or removal of hazardous conditions due to snow, slush and ice on the movement area, by means of a specific format
SPECIAL*	Special meteorological report (in abbreviated plain language)
SSR	Secondary surveillance radar
SST	Supersonic transport
STAR*	Standard (instrument) arrival
TACAN*	UHF tactical air navigation aid
TAF*	Aerodrome forecast
TMA	Terminal control area
UHF	Ultra-high frequency (300 - 3000 MHz)
UIR	Upper flight information region
UTA	Upper control area
UTC	Co-ordinated universal time
VASIS*	Visual approach slope indicator system
VDF	VHF direction finding station
VFR	Visual flight rules
VHF	Very high frequency (30 - 300 MHz)
VIP	Very important person
VMC	Visual meteorological conditions
VOLMET*	Meteorological information for aircraft in flight
VOR	VHF omnidirectional beacon
VORTAC*	VOR and TACAN combined

Index